Developing Literacy
SENTENCE LEVEL

SENTENCE-LEVEL ACTIVITIES FOR THE LITERACY HOUR

year

5

Christine Moorcroft

Series consultant:

Ray Barker

A & C BLACK

Reprinted 1999, 2000, 2001, 2002 (twice)
Published 1999 by
A&C Black Publishers Limited
37 Soho Square, London W1D 3QZ
www.acblack.com

ISBN O-7136-5173-3

The author and publisher would like to thank Ray Barker
and the following teachers for their advice in producing this
series of books: Tracy Adam; Hardip Channa; Lydia Hunt;
Madeleine Madden; Helen Mason; Judith Metcalfe; Heather Morrealy;
Yvonne Newman; Hilary Walden; Fleur Whatley; Annette Wilson.

Extract from *The Hobbit* by J.R.R. Tolkien printed by kind
permission of HarperCollins Publishers Ltd.

A CIP catalogue record for this book is
available from the British Library.

A & C Black uses paper produced with elemental chlorine-free pulp,
harvested from managed sustainable forests.

Printed in Great Britain by
St Edmundsbury Press Ltd, Bury St Edmunds, Suffolk.

Contents

Introduction

Developing Literacy: Sentence Level supports the teaching of reading and writing by providing a series of activities to develop children's understanding that grammar is about the way in which we combine words in sentences to enable the reader to understand what we have written: that writing must make sense to the reader as well as to the writer. To understand grammar, children need to know about the different types of words which make up sentences.

The children learn to examine the effect of their choice of words and to question whether it communicates what they intend. They find out how their choice affects the audience. They also investigate the effect of changing the order of words in a sentence and how to make a text suitable for a particular audience and purpose. They develop their ability to use punctuation to make sentences show variation which would otherwise only be possible in speech.

The activities are designed to be carried out in the time allocated to independent work during the Literacy Hour. They support the objectives of the National Literacy Strategy *Framework for Teaching* at sentence level and incorporate strategies which encourage independent learning – for example, ways in which children can check their own work or that of a partner. Investigating language is given greater emphasis as the series progresses towards **Year 6**.

Year 5 helps children to develop:

- an understanding of elements of grammar introduced in **Years R,1,2,3** and **4** and –

    how the order of words in a sentence affects its meaning;
    the conventions of standard English;
    how to write concisely and accurately;
    how to adapt writing for different audiences;
    how to convert direct to indirect speech and vice versa;
    how to use prepositions to indicate different types of relationships between words.

- an understanding of sentence-construction and punctuation introduced in **Years R,1,2,3** and **4** and –

    punctuation before and after speech marks;
    commas for separating and enclosing units of a sentence;
    colons to signal a list or to separate units of a sentence;
    the punctuation and setting out of dialogue;
    grammatical agreement;
    using different forms of verbs;
    person and the agreement of verbs and pronouns;
    identifying different types of clauses and phrases;
    exploring ambiguities in text;
    re-structuring and abbreviating sentences.

Year 5 encourages the children to investigate language. For example, they investigate the effect of the position of a pronoun on the meaning of a sentence (for instance, comparing 'The explosives were discovered by sniffer dogs. They were hidden in ice cream cartons' with 'The explosives were discovered hidden in ice cream cartons. They were discovered by sniffer dogs'); and they explore the ways in which they can represent spoken dialogue on paper.

The following logos are used to remind the children to use references such as dictionaries and thesauruses:

Extension

Most of the activity sheets end with a challenge (**Now try this!**) which reinforces and extends the children's learning and provides an opportunity for assessment. These more challenging activities might be appropriate for only a few children; it is not expected that the whole class should complete them. On some pages there is space for the children to complete the extension activities, but others will require a notebook or separate sheet of paper.

Organisation

For many of the activities it will be useful to have available scissors, glue, word-banks, a variety of dictionaries and fiction and non-fiction texts. To help teachers to select appropriate learning experiences for their pupils, the activities are grouped into sections within each book. The pages do not require to be presented in the order in which they appear in the book, unless otherwise stated.

Teachers' notes

Brief notes are provided at the bottom of most pages. They give ideas and suggestions for making the most of the activity sheet. They sometimes make suggestions for the whole class introduction, the plenary session or, possibly, for follow-up work using an adapted version of the activity sheet. These notes could be masked before copying.

Structure of the Literacy Hour

The following chart shows an example of the way in which an activity from this book can be used to achieve the required organisation of the Literacy Hour.

Standard English 1 (page 15)

Whole class introduction	15 min
Play pre-recorded samples of non-standard English, for example from television and radio programmes (from regions other than the children's own), and ask the children to explain their meanings. From television programmes they might be familiar with dialects from regions such as Liverpool, Newcastle or the East End of London, but can they identify any incorrect use of grammar, such as double negatives and lack of agreement between pronouns and nouns and between pronouns and verbs? Can they identify any inconsistent use of tenses?	

Whole class activity	15 min
Play 'translators': children in one half of the class are given cards on which is written a sentence in non-standard English; those in the other half have the same sentences written in standard English. They have to find their 'partners' and highlight the differences between the sentences.	

Group work	20 min	Independent work	20 min
The children explore a dialect by listening (using head-phones) to a taped example from radio or television. They make notes of any deviations from standard English.		The others work independently from the activity **Standard English 1** (page 15, **Developing Literacy Sentence Level: Year 5**).	

Whole class plenary session	10 min
The children share the results of their exploration of dialect, presenting some of the common non-standard usages of English alongside their standard forms.	

Using the activity sheets

Grammatical awareness

This section provides activities which develop the children's grammatical awareness by drawing attention to styles of writing, the conventions of standard English and how to convey meaning accurately. It consolidates their understanding of classes of words introduced in previous years and introduces the term 'prepositions'.

Word gaps (page 9) shows the children which words in a sentence are essential to make it a sentence. Here, the verbs are removed (lived, was, meant, had, opened, was, wound, going, called, opened). This activity also helps the children to recognise the words which can be removed and still leave a sentence, but which are essential for the meaning of the sentence to be clear or for it to have the effect intended by the writer; for example, the removal of adjectives from the extract from *The Hobbit* takes away much of the impact of the description.

Shrinking sentences sets 1 and **2** (pages 10–11) consolidate the children's understanding of essential words in a sentence. They should also consider which words are essential grammatically and which are essential to give all the necessary information. 'Dad cooked fish and chips for supper' can be reduced to 'Dad cooked', but the real point of the sentence is lost. The children should identify which classes of words can be removed and still leave a sentence.

In **Sentence pyramids** (page 12) the children can add information about the subject and the verb of each sentence in the form of adjectives, adverbs and prepositions (but not by extending the sentence using connectives).

A different order 1 and **2** (pages 13–14) encourage the children to think about the order in which words appear in sentences. The shapes help them to recognise the relative positions of nouns, verbs and adjectives in sentences which are informative or are in the imperative or interrogative forms.

Standard English 1, 2, 3 and **4** (pages 15–18) include examples of non-standard English which is influenced by dialect. They help the children to recognise the differences between this dialect-influenced English, which can be understood even by people who are unfamiliar with the dialects in question, and standard English. Non-standard English is not necessarily 'wrong' – it is often used in poetry and drama.

Add a phrase (page 19) consolidates the children's understanding of phrases and develops their skills in building sentences by adding phrases to them. Care needs to be taken in the activity suggested in the Teachers' note (using 'why' phrases): 'because the weather was hot' contains a verb – it is therefore a clause, not a phrase; but 'because of the hot weather' contains no verb, and so it is a phrase. Encourage the children to read their sentences aloud to determine if and where commas are needed to make the meaning clear.

Using connectives (page 20) develops the children's skills in building up compound and complex sentences and in linking ideas within a text by using connectives.

A younger audience (page 21) encourages the children to think about the meaning of a text and then to simplify it. They should make notes about all the information contained in each sentence and then write it simply, splitting it into several short sentences if necessary.

Informal and formal (page 22) develops the children's appreciation of the differences between formal and informal text: for example, vocabulary, the use or avoidance of contractions and the length of sentences. Before the activity they should have experience of comparing formal and informal texts and exploring and explaining the differences.

Reported and direct speech 1 and **2** and **An interview** (pages 23–25) develop the children's ability to recognise the ways in which the punctuation of a sentence is altered when it is changed from reported to direct speech; for example, by the addition of a comma before the speech marks and the addition of a question mark. They might need to be reminded about the positions of punctuation marks: full stops, question marks and exclamation marks which follow direct speech precede the final speech marks. The children should also notice any changes of tense and person.

In **Different order, same meaning** (page 26) the children use connectives to combine simple sentences into complex sentences; they also have to alter some of the words when they change the order of the sentences. In **Different order, different meaning** (page 27) the children consider the way in which word order can affect the meaning of a sentence and explain these differences in meaning.

Find the nouns (page 28) revises nouns. Encourage the children to use the 'noun test' to check whether or not a word is a noun and to look for exceptions to the rule. **Abstract noun crossword** (page 29) introduces abstract nouns. It links with word-level work on making nouns from verbs and adjectives. The answers are: **Across 2.** happiness **4.** dread **5.** loss **8.** heat **9.** hardness **12.** jealousy **15.** anger **16.** length **17.** pride ; **Down 1.** width **2.** health **3.** skill **6.** safety **7.** sorrow **10.** sanity **11.** height **13.** speed **14.** rage. **Collective noun mix-up** (page 30) revises collective nouns. Encourage the children to think about the 'feel' of the collective nouns, to investigate collective nouns in reference books such as dictionaries and *Brewer's Dictionary of Phrase and Fable* (Adrian Room, Cassell), and to make up their own descriptive collective nouns.

Pronoun program (page 31) revises personal and possessive pronouns (see **Developing Literacy Sentence Level: Year 4**). **Verbal traffic report** (page 32) revises tenses and agreement between nouns, pronouns and verbs.

Prepositions: of, for and with (page 33) introduces prepositions which are used to show simple relationships. **Place prepositions** (page 34) is about prepositions concerning place. Some children might be able to recognise preposition phrases, such as 'next to', 'in front of' and 'at the back of'. **Time prepositions** (page 35) introduces prepositions concerning time. Some children might be able to recognise preposition phrases, such as 'at the same time as' and 'later/earlier than'.

Sentence-construction and punctuation

Reading with commas, Punctuation changes 1 and **Punctuation changes 2** (pages 37–38) show the children how punctuation is used to help the reader to read sentences in the way in which the writer intended, and that punctuation is used by writers to convey meaning. These activities also revise the use of full stops, commas, exclamation marks, question marks and speech marks.

In **Using colons: sentence units** (page 39), the children have to find the two units which can be combined to make up each sentence, and then to write the sentences, separating the two units with a colon. In each sentence the two units belong together because the first introduces the second (which is an 'identifier'). A colon can also be used to introduce an example (or examples). **Using colons: lists** (page 40) revises the use of a colon to signal the start of a list. **Using semi-colons** (page 41) revises the use of semi-colons to join two sentences so that the second sentence becomes a clause of the first sentence. The children could compare the use of semi-colons and colons; point out the second section of the sentence (is it a clause – does it contain a verb?). They could also compare the ways in which clauses are combined with connectives (see **Developing Literacy Sentence Level: Year 4**).

Apostrophe idioms (page 42) revises the use of apostrophes in contractions and to show possession. Useful reference material includes *Brewer's Dictionary of Phrase and Fable* (Adrian Room, Cassell), *A Dictionary of Idioms and their Origins* (Linda & Roger Flavell, Kyle Cathie), and *The Oxford Book of Quotations* (Oxford University Press).

Dialogue (page 43) encourages the children to investigate the punctuation and setting-out of dialogue.

Back to the future (page 44) opens with one kind of text which is written in the future tense – the children can collect other examples. The activity can be linked with text-level work about different genres.

Using auxiliary verbs draws attention to the way in which auxiliary verbs such as 'am', 'are', 'is', 'was', 'were', 'shall', 'will', 'have' and 'had' are used with other verbs to form tenses.
Active and passive verbs (page 46) introduces the terms 'active' and 'passive'; it does not explain them, but uses visual examples to demonstrate them. Before the children begin the activity, read the examples with them and ask them to describe the active and passive form of a verb. **Interrogative forms of verbs** (page 47) is about the changes which are made to verbs when they are made into their interrogative forms: the subject and verb are reversed and, in the past tense, just the auxiliary verb and the subject are reversed, or the verb is changed and an auxiliary verb is added. **Imperative forms of verbs** and **Instructions** (pages 48–49) are linked with text-level work on writing instructions. The children could collect examples of imperatives from everyday experience, including advertisements, notices, instructions and recipes.

Person to person (page 50) consolidates the children's understanding of the 'person' in which a text is written (see **Developing Literacy Word Level: Year 4**).

From voice to paper 1 and **2** (pages 51–52) develop the children's ability to represent dialogue in text in a way which tells the reader when there is a change of speaker, how the words are spoken, what the speaker does, and about his or her facial expression and gestures.

Advertisement sentences (page 53) encourages the children to explore the use of text which is made up of incomplete sentences. Having re-written the texts in complete sentences, the children could compare the two versions and explain why texts of this type are often written in this way.

Summarising (page 54) develops the children's skills in writing concisely in complete sentences and in producing summaries and headlines as incomplete sentences.

At a glance (page 55) shows the children one way in which they can communicate information briefly and effectively; other devices which they could use include bullet points or numbering (for lists), arranging information in columns (for classified lists) and flow-charts (for instructions in which there are choices).

Sleeker sentences (page 56) helps to give children a 'feel' for texts which read well, and develops their ability to write complex sentences.

Sentence-building game (page 57) is played like consequences. It draws the children's attention to a common pattern of word-order for sentences. Other ways of ordering the different classes of words might work (for example, adjective, adjective, noun, adverb, verb, noun) but many will not (for example, where the adverb is placed at the start).

In **Re-ordering sentences** (page 58) the sentences which the children are asked to change have been constructed very simply using connectives. This activity develops their ability to construct long sentences in a more sophisticated way. Encourage them to use words like 'having', 'after' and 'before', and to convert verbs into their passive forms.

Before they attempt **Types of phrases** (page 59) the children should be able to identify a phrase (see **Developing Literacy Sentence Level: Year 4**). Phrases can act as different parts of speech; noun phrases and adjectival phrases are used in this activity. To make each sentence the children need to add a verb.

Clause links (page 60) helps the children to write interesting sentences by using clauses. Some children might need more practice in writing sentences which contain only one clause (simple sentences). In this activity they work with sentences which contain more than one main clause ('compound sentences' if both clauses are main clauses and 'complex sentences' if one or more of the clauses is a subordinate clause – see page 61). **Main clause** (page 61) helps the children to recognise the main clause in a sentence. A sentence can have two or more main clauses if these clauses are of equal grammatical level; for example, 'He baked a cake and made a pot of tea'. Where one clause depends on another for sense, it is a subordinate clause (for example, 'While the cat is away the mice can play'). **Clause sandwiches** (page 62) consolidates the children's understanding of the use of commas to surround part of a sentence (see **Developing Literacy Sentence Level: Year 4**) and introduces embedded clauses (clauses placed within other clauses).

In **Ambiguity** (page 63) the children consider the two possible meanings of ambiguous signs and headlines and develop their skills in accurate writing. In many cases it is easy to tell which meaning is intended because one of them sounds silly.

Ambiguous pronouns (page 64) develops the children's skills in writing with precision. In each example it is not clear, grammatically, to which noun a pronoun refers, although only one option makes sense.

Glossary of terms used

abbreviation A shortened form. Sometimes an apostrophe is used to denote letters which are omitted; for example, *can't*, *doesn't* and *don't*.

active When a verb is active the subject of the sentence performs the action; for example, *Dan built a wall.*

adjective A word which describes (qualifies) a noun; for example, *big, sweet, soft.*

adjective phrase or **adjectival phrase** A phrase which acts as an adjective; for example, *The dog with the long ears.*

adverb A word which qualifies a verb; for example, *sadly, quickly.*

adverbial phrase A phrase which acts as an adverb; for example, *He slept in his chair, She walked up the hill.*

agreement The way in which linked words agree with one another in terms of person, gender, singular or plural, and tense. Examples: (person) *I ride my bike, He rides his bike*; (gender) *his, her, she, he, it;* (singular/plural) *The boys put on their coats;* (tense) *come* (present), *came* (past).

ambiguity This occurs when text has more than one possible meaning.

antonym A word which has the opposite meaning to another.

apostrophe (') A punctuation mark which denotes the omission of a letter or letters, and the possessive form of a noun (which is, in fact, a contraction of a defunct combination of the noun and possessive pronoun: *Jim's = Jim his*).

auxiliary verb One of a small group of verbs which combines with a main verb to make a tense, or to make the main verb passive; for example, *We were walking to school, I have eaten the cake, She was bitten by a dog.*

clause A group of words which is a distinct part of a sentence and can act as a sentence. A clause includes a verb.

colon (:) A punctuation mark mainly used to introduce a list or an identification (information which is needed to answer a question implied in the first part of the sentence); for example, *We saw three kinds of tree: an oak, an elm and a rowan.*

comma (,) A punctuation mark which is used to separate or surround parts of a sentence and items in a list.

complex sentence A sentence which contains a main clause and at least one subordinate clause.

compound sentence A sentence which contains more than one main clause.

conjunction A word used to link sentences or clauses or to connect words within the same phrase: for example, *and, because, but, later.*

connective A word (or phrase) which makes a connection between one phrase, clause, sentence or paragraph and another. A connective can be a conjunction or an adverb (for example, *finally*), a prepositional expression (for example, *in other words*) or a pronoun (for example, 'she' in the following: *Where is the girl who was going to bring the books? She is over there.*)

contraction A shortened form (using an apostrophe to denote omitted letters) of a word or words: for example, *don't, wouldn't.*

embedded clause A clause which is set within another clause, and is usually preceded and followed by commas; for example, *The old man, who was unsteady on his feet, staggered along the road.*

exclamation mark (!) A punctuation mark used after an exclamation.

genre A specific type of writing or other medium of communication; for example, legend, newspaper story or poem.

imperative The form of a verb which is used for giving orders, commands or instructions; for example, *Please wipe your feet.*

interrogative The form of a verb used in questions.

main clause A clause which makes sense on its own, logically as well as grammatically; for example, *I shall write to you as soon as I know when the wedding is to be.*

noun phrase A group of words which acts as a noun; for example, *A group of people chatted by the gate.*

object The recipient of an action: for example, *Mum read the newspaper.*

order A sentence which gives an instruction; for example, *Keep off the grass.*

passive The form of a verb which is used when the subject has the action done to him, her or it; for example, *She was bitten by a dog.* Sometimes the agent who or which carries out the activity is not given; for example, *heads shall roll.*

person A text may be written in the first person: for example, (singular) *I went, I am,* (plural) *we went, we are;* the second person; for example, (singular and plural) *you went, you are;* or the third person; for example, (singular) *he/she/it went, he/she/it is,* (plural) *they went, they are.*

personal pronoun (see **pronoun**).

phrase A group of words which act as a unit; for example, *the old man went to sleep in his chair* (see also **adjective phrase** and **noun phrase**).

possessive pronoun (see **pronoun**).

possessive The form of a noun which shows ownership: *Jane's, the girl's, the children's, the boys'.*

preposition A word which describes a relationship between one noun or pronoun (or noun or pronoun phrase) and another; for example, *under, on, before.*

pronoun A word used instead of a noun; for example: (personal pronouns) *I, you, he, she, it, we, they;* (dependent possessive pronouns) *my, your, her, his, its, our, their;* (independent possessive pronouns) *mine, yours, his, hers, its, ours, theirs.*

semi-colon (;) A punctuation mark used to separate clauses of equal importance in a sentence.

statement A sentence which gives information; for example, *He likes reading.*

subject The subject of a verb is the person or thing which does it; for example, *Mum read the newspaper.*

subordinate clause A clause which does not make sense, logically, on its own – it depends for its meaning on a main clause; for example, *I shall write to you as soon as I know when the wedding is to be.*

tense The tense of a verb shows when it happens; for example, (present) *she writes/she is writing,* (past) *she wrote/she has written,* (future) *she will write.*

Word gaps

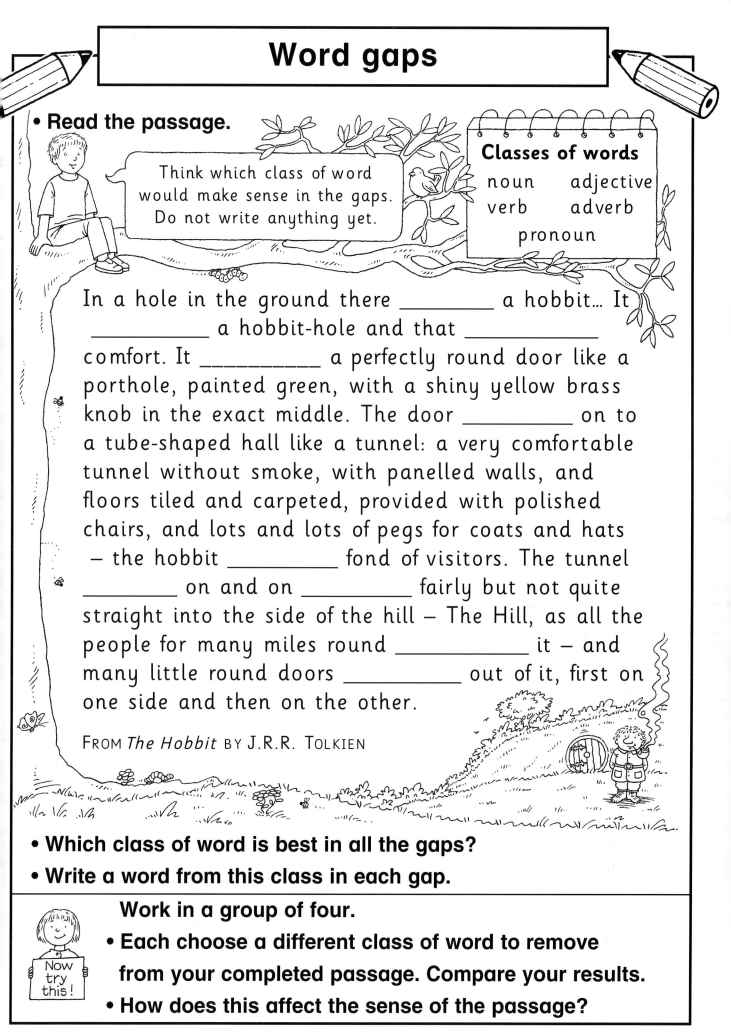

- **Read the passage.**

Think which class of word would make sense in the gaps. Do not write anything yet.

Classes of words

noun   adjective
verb   adverb
    pronoun

In a hole in the ground there _____ a hobbit… It _____ a hobbit-hole and that _____ comfort. It _____ a perfectly round door like a porthole, painted green, with a shiny yellow brass knob in the exact middle. The door _____ on to a tube-shaped hall like a tunnel: a very comfortable tunnel without smoke, with panelled walls, and floors tiled and carpeted, provided with polished chairs, and lots and lots of pegs for coats and hats – the hobbit _____ fond of visitors. The tunnel _____ on and on _____ fairly but not quite straight into the side of the hill – The Hill, as all the people for many miles round _____ it – and many little round doors _____ out of it, first on one side and then on the other.

FROM *The Hobbit* BY J.R.R. TOLKIEN

- **Which class of word is best in all the gaps?**
- **Write a word from this class in each gap.**

Work in a group of four.

- **Each choose a different class of word to remove from your completed passage. Compare your results.**
- **How does this affect the sense of the passage?**

Now try this!

Teachers' note In groups, different children could delete different classes of word from a photocopied passage from a book. They could notice whose passage still makes sense and explain the effects of removing the words.

Developing Literacy
Sentence Level Year 5
© A & C Black 1999

Shrinking sentences: set 1

Instructions

Play in a group of three. One of you acts as 'timer'.

The other two players should each take away words from each sentence to leave the shortest possible sentence.

They write the new sentences they have made. After 30 seconds, the 'timer' asks how many words they have in their new sentences. The player with fewer words reads them out. This player scores a point if the words are a sentence, or loses a point if they are not.

You need a kitchen timer, stop-watch or stop-clock.

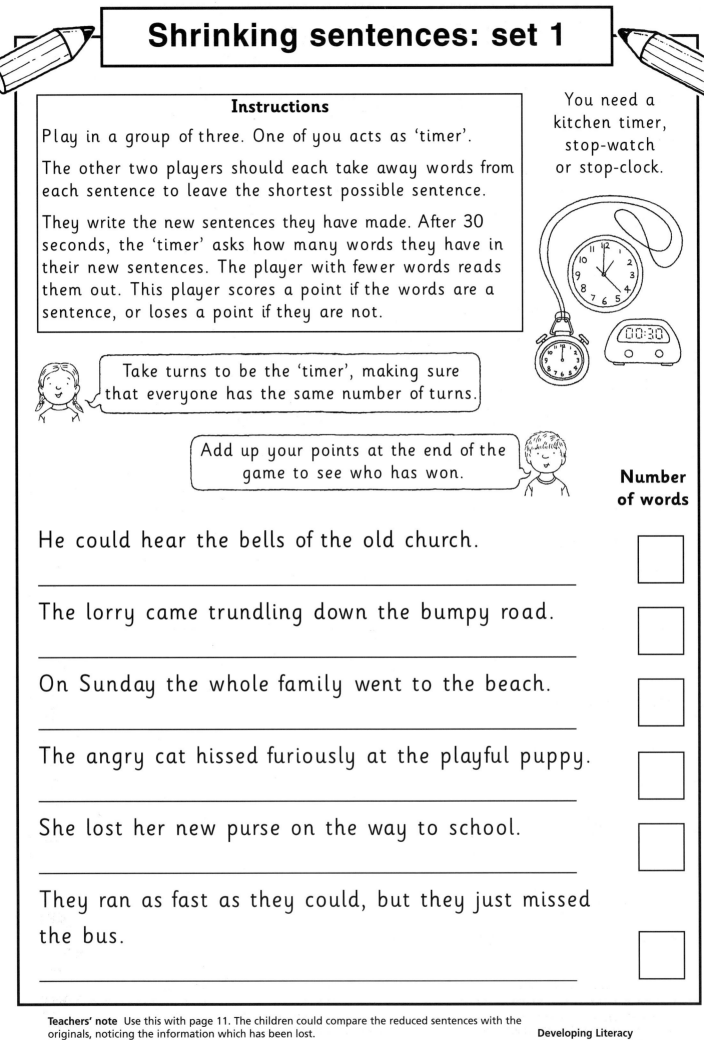

Take turns to be the 'timer', making sure that everyone has the same number of turns.

Add up your points at the end of the game to see who has won.

Number of words

He could hear the bells of the old church.

The lorry came trundling down the bumpy road.

On Sunday the whole family went to the beach.

The angry cat hissed furiously at the playful puppy.

She lost her new purse on the way to school.

They ran as fast as they could, but they just missed the bus.

Teachers' note Use this with page 11. The children could compare the reduced sentences with the originals, noticing the information which has been lost.

Developing Literacy
Sentence Level Year 5
© A & C Black 1999

Shrinking sentences: set 2

Whenever Jason played football he wore his red jersey.

_____

In the meadow there were twelve black and white cows.

_____

Dad cooked fish and chips for supper.

_____

In the middle of the night there was a loud crash.

_____

One morning Bhavna awoke to see a huge bunch of flowers on the dressing table.

_____

During our holiday in France we watched a famous cycle race, the Tour de France.

_____

Sixteen children came running down the hill laughing and talking.

_____

We wondered why the woman wore a woollen coat on such a hot sunny day.

_____

Teachers' note Use this with page 10. As an extension, photocopy a passage from a book on which the children highlight words which can be deleted yet leave a sentence. Discuss the effects of removing these words. The text might still consist of sentences, but its meaning is lost.

**Developing Literacy
Sentence Level Year 5
© A & C Black 1999**

Sentence pyramids

• **Add words to each sentence to give more information.**

A plane landed.

A passenger plane landed.

A passenger plane landed on the beach.

She slept.

He came.

The man sang.

The girl cried.

Now try this!

• **Make sentence pyramids with four layers from**

| A horse neighed. | A bird sang. | A bell rang. |

Teachers' note The children could be given sentences like those on the pyramids, and challenged to add as much information as they can (without extending the sentences by using words such as 'and' or 'then'). They could go on to make pyramids of five or six layers.

Developing Literacy
Sentence Level Year 5
© A & C Black 1999

12

A different order 1

- Make up sentences using the words in the shapes.
- Keep the words in the order shown.
- Use any of the extra words as many times as you want, but do not add any others.

Extra words

the   a   it

in   to

Key

noun   verb

adjective

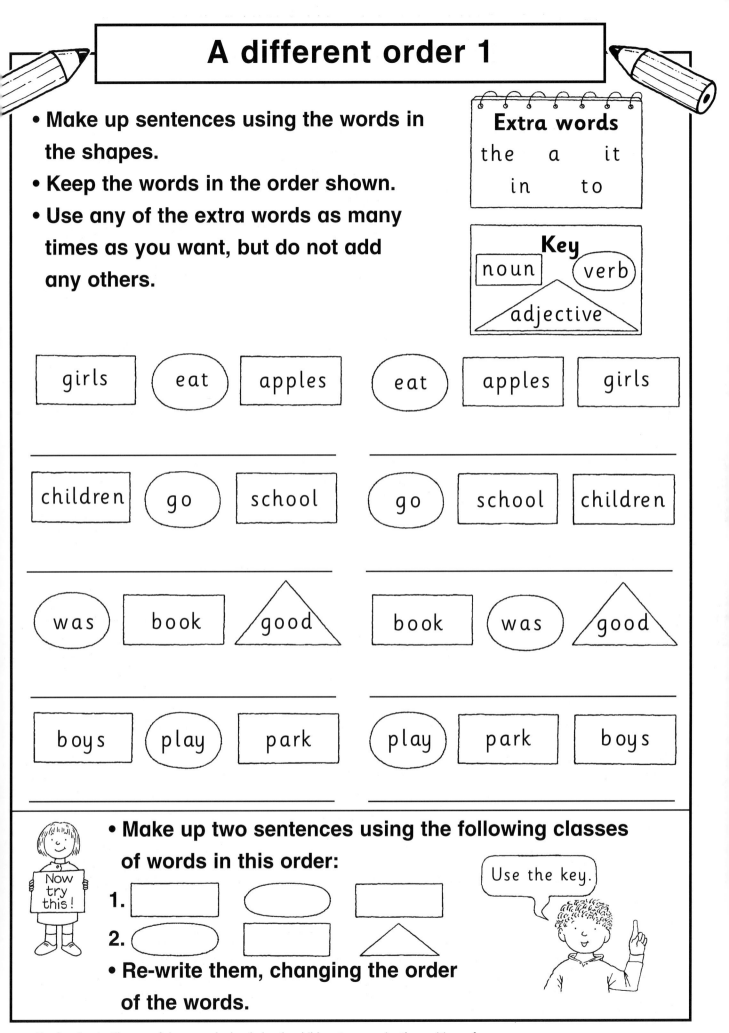

girls   eat   apples   eat   apples   girls

children   go   school   go   school   children

was   book   good   book   was   good

boys   play   park   play   park   boys

Now try this!

- Make up two sentences using the following classes of words in this order:

Use the key.

1.

2.

- Re-write them, changing the order of the words.

Teachers' note The use of shapes and a key helps the children to recognise the positions of different classes of word in a sentence. For differentiation, more difficult words could be substituted.

Developing Literacy
Sentence Level Year 5
© A & C Black 1999

A different order 2

- **Write sentences, keeping the words in the order given.**
- **Change the word-order and write new sentences. Draw the shapes.**

Extra words

the	a	an
in	to	at
is	does	did

You might have to change the verb-endings.

Key

noun   verb   adverb   adjective

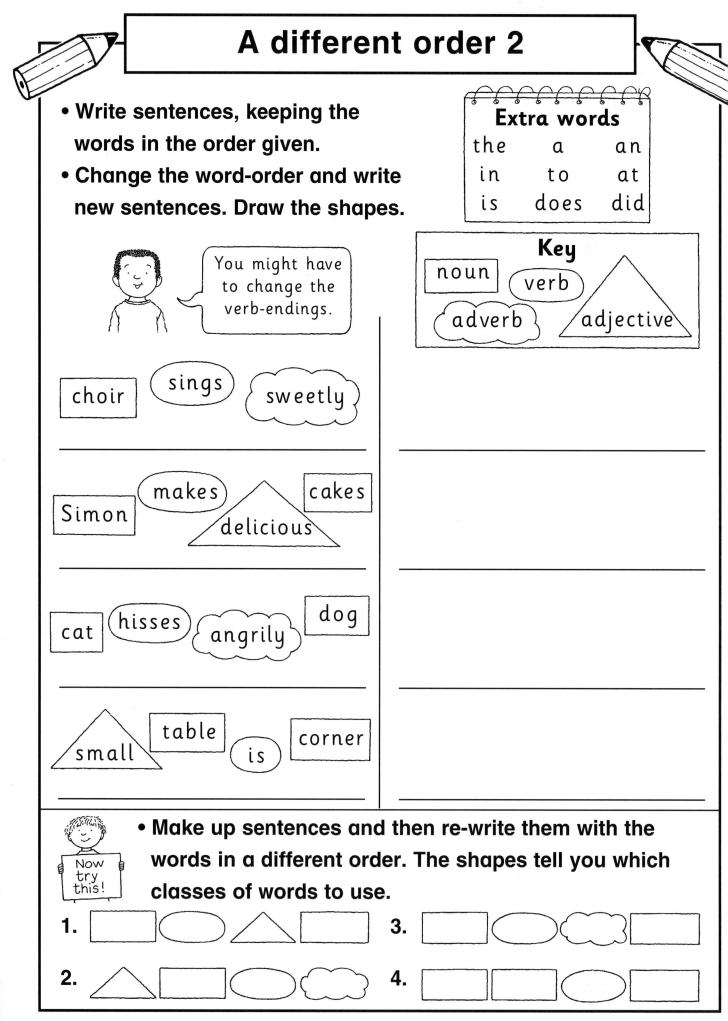

choir   sings   sweetly

Simon   makes   delicious   cakes

cat   hisses   angrily   dog

small   table   is   corner

- **Make up sentences and then re-write them with the words in a different order. The shapes tell you which classes of words to use.**

Now try this!

1. ▭ ⬭ △ ▭

2. △ ▭ ⬭ ☁

3. ▭ ⬭ ☁ ▭

4. ▭ ▭ ⬭ ▭

Teachers' note On a photocopied passage from a book, the children could highlight the words which can be deleted yet still leave sentences. Discuss the effects of removing these words. The text might still have sentences, but does it make sense?

Developing Literacy
Sentence Level Year 5
© A & C Black 1999

Standard English 1

These people are speaking in their local dialects.

• Write their words in standard English.

We was robbed.

The children were all sat on the carpet.

I should have went to the dentist.

It were a little red car.

I seen him in the shop.

I bin come to see the exhibition.

My mum do like flowers.

That's what I does - I ignores them.

I done my homework before supper.

• Which class of words has to be changed to turn the people's speech into standard English?

• Write four other examples of speech in dialects, in which this class of word is changed from standard English.

Now try this!

Teachers' note The children should know that a class of word means a noun, verb, adjective, adverb and so on.

Developing Literacy
Sentence Level Year 5
© A & C Black 1999

Standard English 2

- **Underline the words which need to be changed to turn this conversation into standard English.**

'I don't want none of that fish,' said the woman to the fishmonger. 'That plaice ain't got no spots.'

'It was swimming in the sea yesterday,' he replied. 'I can't get it no fresher than that.'

'It looks as if it ain't seen no water for months,' she answered. 'Ain't you got no cod?'

'Yes, there's this lovely cod fillet; you won't get no better fish in the whole town,' he answered.

'That ain't nowhere near big enough,' she said. 'Ain't you got no bigger pieces?'

'Sorry, but that's the last piece I got. It was so good that I knew there wouldn't be none left by the afternoon.'

- **Re-write the conversation in standard English.**
- **Underline the words you changed.**

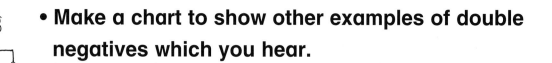

- **Make a chart to show other examples of double negatives which you hear.**

Double negative	Standard English

Teachers' note Some children might need help in spotting that the main deviation from standard English is the use of double negatives, as well as the use of 'ain't' instead of 'isn't/is not' or 'haven't/ have not'.

Developing Literacy
Sentence Level Year 5
© A & C Black 1999

Standard English 3

- Underline the words which are not standard English.
- Write each person's speech in standard English.

Teachers' note The children could also make notes about other uses of words in non-standard
English which they hear.

Developing Literacy
Sentence Level Year 5
© A & C Black 1999

Standard English 4

Be a dialect translator!

• Use the glossary to help you to translate local dialect speech into standard English.

Glossary
bap - bread roll
butty - sandwich
made up - delighted
neeps - mashed turnip
outwith - outside
nowt - nothing
starbob - starling
swither - hesitate
tatty - potato

You'll never get anything done if you keep swithering.

_____

_____

There's nowt wrong with her.

Starbobs were eating the scraps from the kitchen.

There are woods outwith the town.

_____

_____

I'd like a jam butty, please.

_____

I'd like a bap filled with salad.

_____

I'd like tatties with neeps.

Mum was made up with her present.

_____

_____

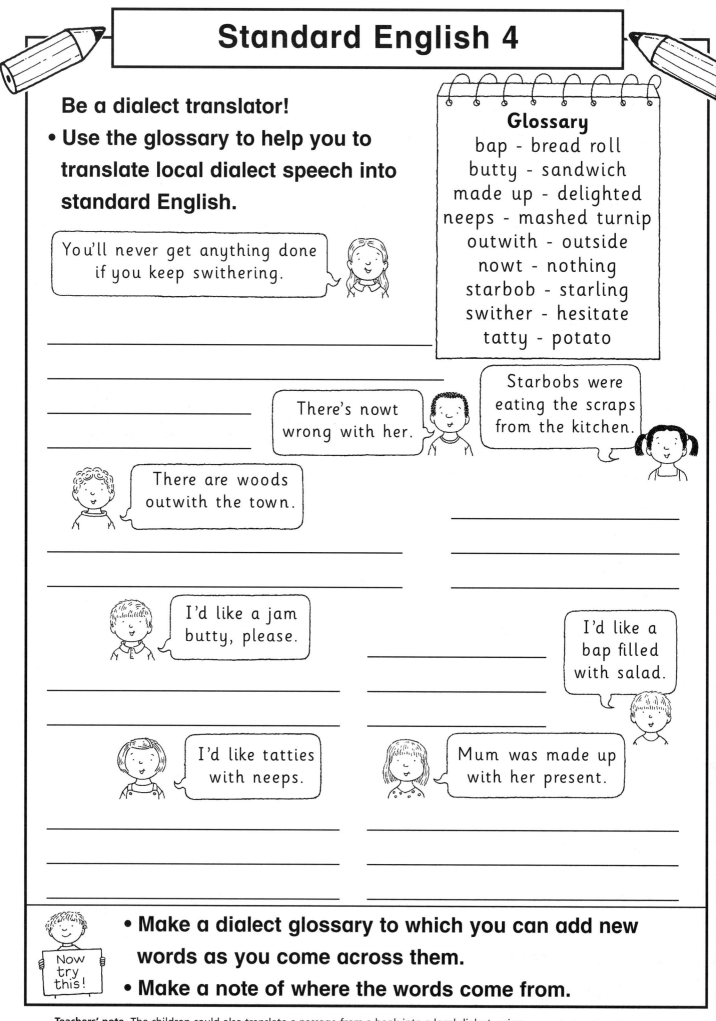

Now try this!

• **Make a dialect glossary to which you can add new words as you come across them.**
• **Make a note of where the words come from.**

Teachers' note The children could also translate a passage from a book into a local dialect, using dialect words and the grammatical constructions about which they have learned. They could read it aloud and compare it with the original.

Developing Literacy
Sentence Level Year 5
© A & C Black 1999

Add a phrase

A <u>phrase</u> is a group of words which does not contain a verb.

• Use a phrase to add information to each sentence.

Phrases which tell you <u>how</u>	Phrases which tell you <u>where</u>	Phrases which tell you <u>when</u>
from coloured tissue paper with the help of his brother by adding 30, then taking away 1	at Sutton Hoo in an etymological dictionary	on Saturday in the fifteenth century

Sentence	Sentence plus phrase
1. Robert made some paper flowers...	
2. He pushed his car into the garage...	
3. It was her sister's wedding...	
4. Leonardo da Vinci was an Italian artist...	
5. Archaeologists found the remains of an Anglo-Saxon ship...	
6. You can add 29 to any number...	
7. The children found out about the derivations of words...	

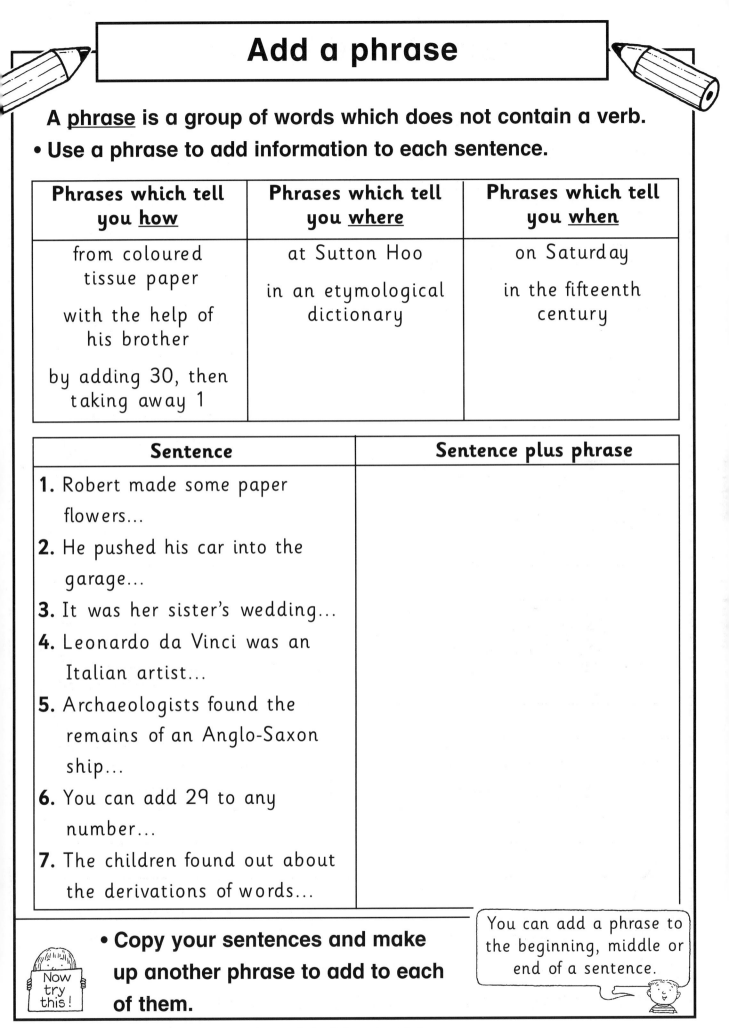

Now try this!

• Copy your sentences and make up another phrase to add to each of them.

You can add a phrase to the beginning, middle or end of a sentence.

Teachers' note The children could also add phrases which tell them <u>why</u>. Ask them to suggest words with which to begin such phrases; for example, because of, so that, in order, since, to.

Developing Literacy
Sentence Level Year 5
© A & C Black 1999

Using connectives

A **connective** is a word or phrase which is used to link ideas.

- Circle the connectives and underline the ideas which they join.

Some common connectives are: and, but, or, as soon as, then, finally, nevertheless.

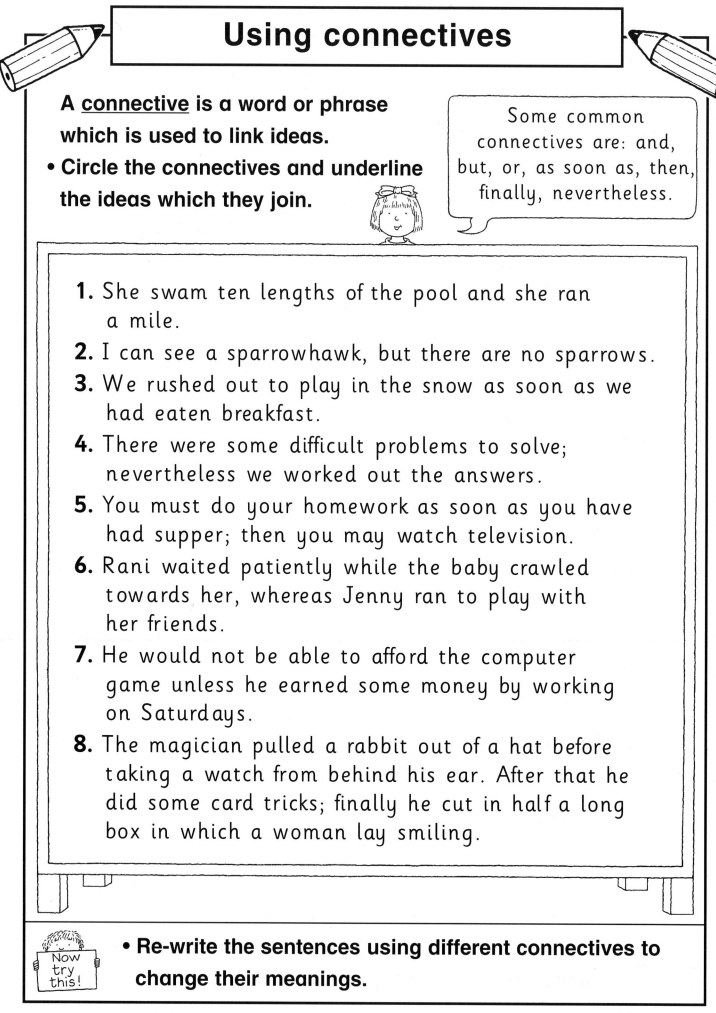

1. She swam ten lengths of the pool and she ran a mile.

2. I can see a sparrowhawk, but there are no sparrows.

3. We rushed out to play in the snow as soon as we had eaten breakfast.

4. There were some difficult problems to solve; nevertheless we worked out the answers.

5. You must do your homework as soon as you have had supper; then you may watch television.

6. Rani waited patiently while the baby crawled towards her, whereas Jenny ran to play with her friends.

7. He would not be able to afford the computer game unless he earned some money by working on Saturdays.

8. The magician pulled a rabbit out of a hat before taking a watch from behind his ear. After that he did some card tricks; finally he cut in half a long box in which a woman lay smiling.

Now try this!

- **Re-write the sentences using different connectives to change their meanings.**

Teachers' note The children could compile a 'connectives bank' in which connectives are classified according to type; for example, connectives which add information, give a contrast, add reasons, add methods and so on.

Developing Literacy
Sentence Level Year 5
© A & C Black 1999

A younger audience

- **Read the text.**
- **Re-write it for a six-year-old.**

Think about short sentences, simple words and explanations of terms.

Text	Change to:
Magnets, which are themselves metallic, attract most, but not all, metallic objects, but no other materials.	Magnets are made of metal. They only attract metal things. They do not attract all metals. Attract means pick up or pull.
The objects which they attract, (for example, nails and pins), usually contain iron.	
Non-magnetic metallic objects include aluminium drink cans, brass drawing pins and gold rings.	
A magnet can attract a magnetic material which is covered in a non-magnetic material: for example, a tin-coated steel soup can or a painted steel knitting needle.	
The attraction of magnets is strongest at their poles.	

Now try this!

- **Discuss your ideas with a partner.**
- **Edit your new text using a different coloured pen.**
- **Write and illustrate the text for a six-year-old.**

Teachers' note The children should first discuss each sentence to decide what information it gives and how the same information can be written more simply. They could compare books written for six-year-olds with those written for older children. For the extension activity, they will need extra time, perhaps homework time.

Developing Literacy
Sentence Level Year 5
© A & C Black 1999

Informal and formal

- **Write each extract in a more formal way.**
- **Notice its purpose and audience.**

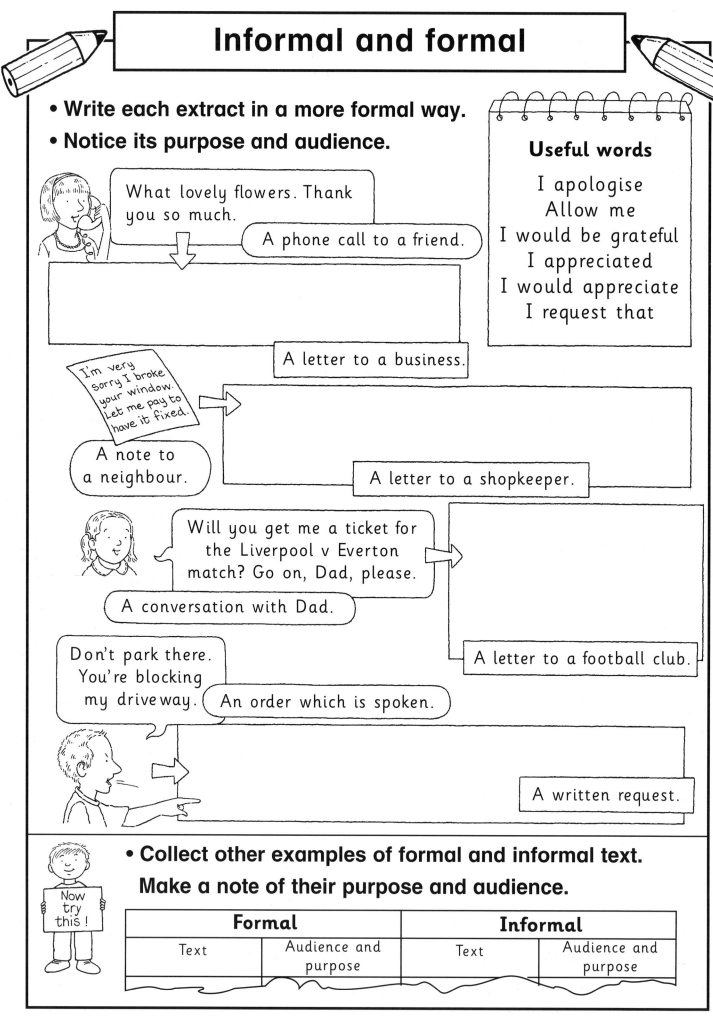

Useful words

I apologise
Allow me
I would be grateful
I appreciated
I would appreciate
I request that

What lovely flowers. Thank you so much.

A phone call to a friend.

A letter to a business.

I'm very sorry I broke your window. Let me pay to have it fixed.

A note to a neighbour.

A letter to a shopkeeper.

Will you get me a ticket for the Liverpool v Everton match? Go on, Dad, please.

A conversation with Dad.

A letter to a football club.

Don't park there. You're blocking my driveway.

An order which is spoken.

A written request.

- **Collect other examples of formal and informal text.**
  Make a note of their purpose and audience.

Now try this !

Formal		Informal	
Text	Audience and purpose	Text	Audience and purpose

Teachers' note The children can compare informal and formal texts, noting the vocabulary used and the simplicity or complexity of the sentences.

Developing Literacy
Sentence Level Year 5
© A & C Black 1999

Reported and direct speech 1

- **Match the reported speech to the direct speech.**
- **Circle the changes in punctuation.**

Notice changes in tense, person, punctuation and in the words used.

The manager asked us not to sit on the window ledge.

The children's mother insisted that they put their toys away immediately.

He told us that there was a sheep in our garden.

She asked for a cup of tea.

He asked if he might enter the building.

James ordered Rover to lie down.

Their neighbours waved and called out a greeting.

"May I have a cup of tea, please?" she asked.

"Please do not sit on the window ledge," said the manager.

"Lie down!" cried James to Rover.

"Hello!" called their neighbours, waving.

The children's mother said, "Put your toys away now!"

He said, "There is a sheep in your garden."

"May I enter the building, please?" he asked.

- **List all the ways in which direct speech must be changed to write it as reported speech.**

Now try this!

- **Write five examples of direct speech.**
- **Re-write them as reported speech.**

Teachers' note As well as noticing changes, the children should notice any words or punctuation marks which they have added or removed.

Developing Literacy
Sentence Level Year 5
© A & C Black 1999

Reported and direct speech 2

• Write about what these people said, as direct speech and as reported speech.

Direct speech		Reported speech
	I like apples.	
	What time is it, please?	
	Get out of my apple tree!	
	I would like a tuna pizza, please.	
	May I come in?	

• **Write this passage as direct speech:**

The teacher asked Amy if she had finished her work; Amy said she had. She asked if she might have a new notebook - hers was full. The teacher praised her for working hard.

Teachers' note The children could also write extracts from drama scripts as both direct and reported speech.

Developing Literacy
Sentence Level Year 5
© A & C Black 1999

An interview

- **Read the journalist's notes from part of an interview.**
- **Re-write them as direct speech.**

Tim Johnson (journalist)   Dr May Sung (medical doctor)   Rose Bull (dairy farmer)   Johnny Appleseed (fruit grower)

TJ	Greeted everyone, thanked them for coming. Like to start with Dr MS - What do you think is healthy diet?
MS	A mixture - not too much of anything. Good variety - meat, fish, veg, fruit, cereals, dairy produce, pulses.
TJ	You wouldn't recommend any one special food?
MS	No - well, perhaps fruit and green veg.
TJ	What is special about them? **MS** Prevent cancer.
TJ	What about you, RB? Do you agree? **RB** No - eat them by all means, but dairy produce has calcium - needed for teeth + bones.
JA	Fruit needed for vitamins.

"Good evening everyone," said Tim Johnson. "Thank you for coming here today. I would like to start with Dr. May Sung - what do you think is a healthy diet?"

_____

_____

_____

_____

_____

_____

_____

_____

_____

Now try this!

- **Re-write the interview as reported speech.**

Tim Johnson greeted his guests and thanked them for coming.

Teachers' note The children should notice that the journalist has used abbreviations in his notes and missed out words, for speed.

Developing Literacy
Sentence Level Year 5
© A & C Black 1999

Different order, same meaning

- **Re-write each set of simple sentences, in a different order, as one complex sentence.**

Useful words

however	but
having	and
although	who
because	when

You might need to change some of the words.

Make sure that your new sentences make sense.

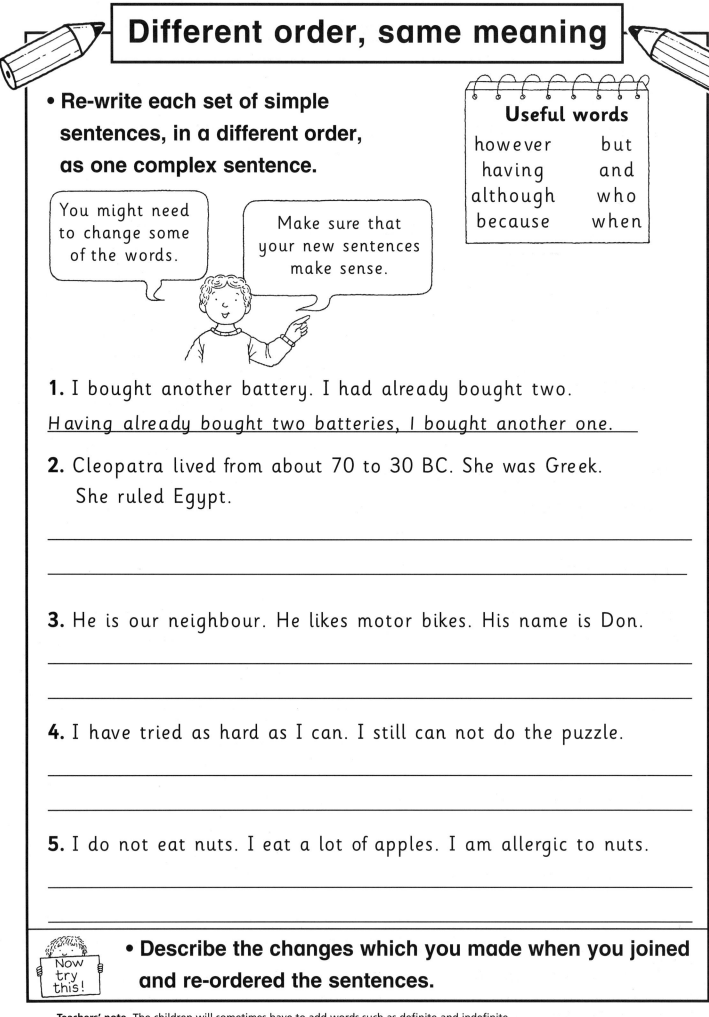

1. I bought another battery. I had already bought two.

Having already bought two batteries, I bought another one.

2. Cleopatra lived from about 70 to 30 BC. She was Greek. She ruled Egypt.

_____

_____

3. He is our neighbour. He likes motor bikes. His name is Don.

_____

_____

4. I have tried as hard as I can. I still can not do the puzzle.

_____

_____

5. I do not eat nuts. I eat a lot of apples. I am allergic to nuts.

_____

_____

Now try this!

- **Describe the changes which you made when you joined and re-ordered the sentences.**

Teachers' note The children will sometimes have to add words such as definite and indefinite articles as well as the words on the notepad. They should also notice the changes they have made to verbs.

Developing Literacy
Sentence Level Year 5
© A & C Black 1999

Different order, different meaning

The meaning of a sentence depends on the order of the words.

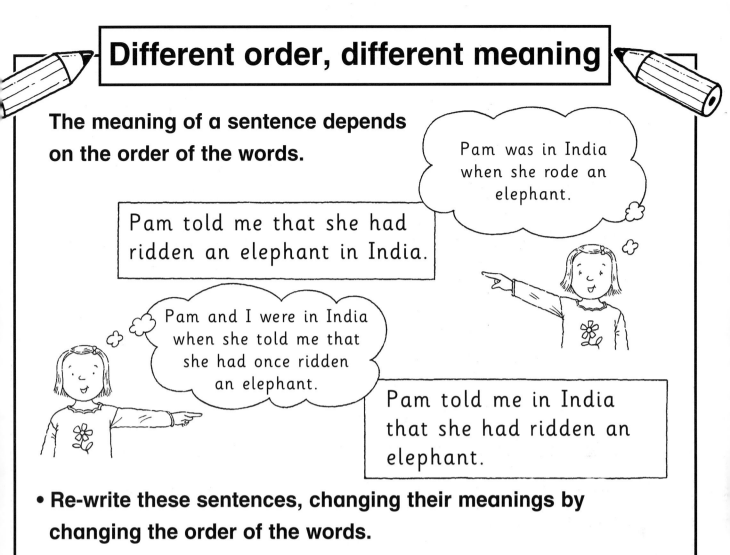

Pam was in India when she rode an elephant.

Pam told me that she had ridden an elephant in India.

Pam and I were in India when she told me that she had once ridden an elephant.

Pam told me in India that she had ridden an elephant.

• **Re-write these sentences, changing their meanings by changing the order of the words.**

My hair needs cutting badly.

_____

She lost her locket containing a picture of her mother in Newcastle one Saturday evening.

_____

_____

_____

I read a book written by Dickens last week.

_____

Hooting in the trees he heard an owl.

_____

Now try this!

• **Explain the differences in meaning between each pair of sentences.**

Teachers' note The children could look for other examples of sentences whose meanings can be changed by altering the word-order.

**Developing Literacy
Sentence Level Year 5
© A & C Black 1999**

Find the nouns

• **Read the passage and underline the nouns.**

Do the 'noun test' on the words which you think are nouns.

Remember - some words can be used as nouns or other parts of speech. Only underline them if they are used as nouns.

The Mughals came to India from central Asia, seizing land to create a huge kingdom. Babur, a prince from the land now known as Tajikistan, had been the first of their leaders to fight his way through the pass between the Hindu Kush mountains and the Himalayas, in 1519. He captured a large area (mainly the area now known as the Punjab) just south of the Himalayas, and also the cities of Delhi and Agra. Babur created gardens in Agra, planted with trees and flowers: cool, green places with pools and fountains, in a country of glaring hot sunshine. The remains of the Aram Bagh (Garden of Repose) can still be seen there. Like most Mughal formal gardens it was square, with paved paths which led from the centre to the four corners.

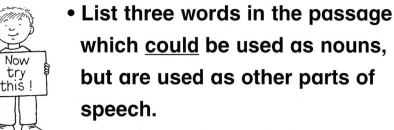

• **List three words in the passage which <u>could</u> be used as nouns, but are used as other parts of speech.**
• **Record them on a chart.**

Word	Noun test	Used as

Teachers' note Revise proper nouns if necessary. Some children might be able to use other tests for nouns: they can be preceded by a possessive pronoun and described by adjectives and they can be the subject or object of a verb.

Developing Literacy
Sentence Level Year 5
© A & C Black 1999

Abstract noun crossword

Abstract nouns are words for things which you can not see or touch.

> **Examples:** truth, freedom, sadness, kindness.

- **Complete the crossword with abstract nouns.**

> Try the noun test on abstract nouns: put the, my, your, his, her, its, our or their in front of them.

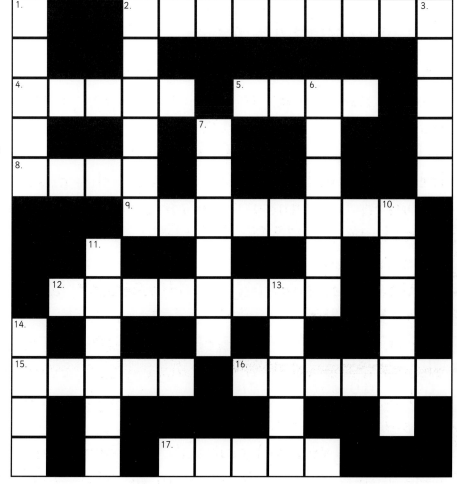

Across

- **2.** The opposite of sadness (9).
- **4.** Great fear (5).
- **5.** The noun which comes from the verb 'to lose' (4).
- **8.** 'Hotness' (4).
- **9.** The opposite of softness (8).
- **12.** Envy (8).
- **15.** Fury (5).
- **16.** The measure of how long something is (6).
- **17.** The noun which comes from the adjective 'proud' (5).

Down

- **1.** Breadth (5).
- **2.** The noun from which 'healthy' is made (6).
- **3.** The noun from which 'skilful' is made (5).
- **6.** The opposite of danger (6).
- **7.** Sadness (6).
- **10.** The opposite of madness (6).
- **11.** The measure of how tall something is (6).
- **13.** This can be measured in kilometres per hour or miles per hour (5).
- **14.** Great anger (5).

- **Write sentences using six of the abstract nouns.**

Teachers' note The children should notice that abstract nouns are not usually pluralised.

Developing Literacy
Sentence Level Year 5
© A & C Black 1999

Collective noun mix-up

The collective nouns have been put into the wrong sentences.

- **Underline the collective nouns.**

- **Re-write the sentences, with the correct collective nouns.**

A pack of fish darted past the diver.	
There was a herd of ships entering the harbour.	
Two shoals of footballers ran on to the pitch.	
The corn had been gathered into a flock.	
A hand of geese waddled across the farmyard.	
He dealt the whole team of cards.	
The farmer drove a fleet of cows down the lane.	
An army of bananas hung from a hook in the shop.	
A gaggle of soldiers marched past the queen.	
We watched a sheaf of birds fly over the woods.	

- **Choose five of the above sentences, and describe the mental 'picture' which the correct and incorrect collective nouns gave you.**

Teachers' note The children should consider the 'feel' of each collective noun, even if they do not know the conventional ones: does it 'feel right' in the sentence?

Developing Literacy
Sentence Level Year 5
© A & C Black 1999

Pronoun program

The computer has a bug which replaces pronouns with nouns.

- Re-write the text, using pronouns where they are needed.

You will need to keep **some** nouns for the text to make sense.

Mum asked Karl to help Mum to fix Mum's car. 'Yes,' said Karl. 'When Mum and Karl have fixed Mum's car, Karl will do Karl's homework.'

'Thank you. Mum will make Karl's supper while Karl does Karl's homework,' said Mum. 'Mum will put Sam and May to bed after Sam and May have had Sam's and May's supper.'

'Right – let Mum and Karl get started on Mum's car then,' answered Karl.

Now try this!

- **Circle any other words which you had to change as well as the nouns.**

Teachers' note The children should notice that they have to alter the verbs to agree with the pronouns.

Developing Literacy
Sentence Level Year 5
© A & C Black 1999

Verbal traffic report

The radio crackles every time the traffic reporter uses a verb.

- **Re-write the report, using the correct form of each verb.**

There (**to be**) a few cancelled trains this morning: the 8.45 Liverpool Lime Street to Euston service (**to be**) cancelled; Merseyrail (**to provide**) bus services between Huyton and Broadgreen, where services (**to disrupt**) because of rubbish on the line.

Flights in and out of Liverpool and Manchester (**to run**) normally until this evening; passengers who (**to travel**) after 8pm should (**to check**) for alterations.

On the roads there (**to be**) a few delays; an accident (**to block**) the A 580 at Haydock since 7am and there (**to be**) delays for at least an hour; emergency services have just (**to clear**) the debris from an accident at junction 2 of the M62, and traffic (**to begin**) to move again. The RAC (**to give**) a warning of fog and drivers (**to be warned**) to take extra care.

Now try this!

- **Copy and complete the chart to show the correct forms of the verbs (in the present tense):**

Verb	Correct form		Verb	Correct form	
to cheer	the crowd ____	the people __	to hope	I _____	they _____
to say	she _____	people _____	to know	he _____	we _____
to sing	the choir ____	the birds ___	to listen	the class _____	the children __

Teachers' note The children could first listen to an extract of a traffic report and notice the tenses of the verbs – mainly the present, except for references to causes of problems (past) or for advice about what to do (future).

Developing Literacy
Sentence Level Year 5
© A & C Black 1999

Prepositions: of, for and with

Prepositions join words, phrases and clauses.

Example: a pot <u>of</u> tea

Use dictionaries of idioms and sayings.

• Complete each idiom or saying with one of the prepositions: of, for or with.

chips _____ everything

horses _____ courses

looking _____ a needle in a haystack

good _____ nothing

a penny _____ your thoughts

pride _____ place

take the rough _____ the smooth

making mountains out _____ molehills

dig _____ victory

out _____ the frying pan into the fire

changing _____ the wind

pots _____ money

take it _____ a pinch _____ salt

a pack _____ lies

a slip _____ the tongue

crying _____ laughter

money_____ old rope

birds _____ a feather

a lap _____ honour

playing _____ fire

• **Write six sentences using the prepositions of, for or with.**

Now try this!

Teachers' note The children could collect other examples of idioms and sayings which contain prepositions.

Developing Literacy
Sentence Level Year 5
© A & C Black 1999

33

Place prepositions

A preposition can show <u>where</u> something happens.

Examples:

The cat is <u>on</u> the mat.

The cat is <u>under</u> the mat.

- **Underline the prepositions.**
- **Re-write each sentence, changing the prepositions, to give it a different meaning.**

Useful place prepositions

across	underneath
around	by
below	down
beyond	in
near	into
under	on
within	past
alongside	up

1. The helicopter hovered above the rooftops.

2. Beneath the streets of Chester lie Roman remains.

3. The school is opposite the hospital.

4. He built a high wall around his garden.

5. The cat jumped off the tree and ran along the wall.

6. We strolled through the woods and had a picnic among the trees.

7. Mum was waiting at the door with Dad behind her.

8. We sowed onions between the carrot seeds and sprinkled soil over them.

9. Go through the tunnel and open the gate beside the red door.

10. There is a small bottle on a table behind the gold curtain.

- **Write a sentence which contains three prepositions.**
- **Re-write it in as many different ways as possible, by changing the prepositions.**

Teachers' note The children could compile an alphabetical list of prepositions, beginning with those on this page. They could also arrange prepositions in groups of synonyms or pairs of antonyms.

**Developing Literacy
Sentence Level Year 5
© A & C Black 1999**

Time prepositions

- **A preposition can show a relationship between a thing, an animal or a person and a <u>time</u>.**
- **Write a time preposition in each gap.**
- **Read the sentences.**

Take two tablets _____ meals.

Built —— 1763
There has been a church on this site _____ 1413.

I was born _____ the Second World War.

This centre was opened ____ 14 May 1963 by James Bygg-Cheese.

We need to be there _____ 6pm _____ the latest.

This office is open _____ 9am _____ 5pm (Monday _____ Friday).

Please do not try to leave the train _____ it comes to a standstill.

I have known her _____ she was six.

Now try this!
- **Write sentences containing the time prepositions which you have not used.**

Teachers' note The children could re-write the sentences in the main activity and/or those in the extension activity using different prepositions.

Developing Literacy
Sentence Level Year 5
© A & C Black 1999

35

Reading with commas

• **Read these two sentences aloud.**

> I bought a loaf a cake and a pie.

> I bought a loaf, a cake and a pie.

Notice the difference made by commas.

• **Read the sentences below aloud.**
• **Put commas in the correct places.**
• **Read the sentences aloud again.**

1. Jenny went to the zoo but she did not see the dolphins.
2. Under the floorboards in a small wooden box they found a necklace.
3. She made some soup poached a fish and baked a pie.
4. In Joe's pocket there were two conkers some string a shell and five pence.
5. The children looked everywhere but they could not find the lost purse.
6. It was a cold wet misty day so we did not go for a walk.
7. There was a large table in the room with chairs all round it but nobody ever sat there.
8. She strolled quietly down the lane looking at the daffodils until she reached the paddock.
9. We saw an owl last night perched on a branch of the plane tree but it is not there tonight.
10. Bring a pan of water to the boil lower in the egg on a spoon and boil the egg for four minutes.

Now try this!

• **Look in books for six sentences which have commas.**
• **Read them aloud with and without the commas.**

Teachers' note The children could explore the use of commas in a shared text, describing how the commas help the reader.

Developing Literacy
Sentence Level Year 5
© A & C Black 1999

Punctuation changes 1

Changing the punctuation can alter the meaning of a sentence.

• **Change the punctuation to alter the meaning of these sentences:**

DANGER? NO. SKATING ALLOWED.

DANGER! NO SKATING ALLOWED

Use commas, full stops, question marks and exclamation marks.

FOR SALE: Bicycle by lady with collapsible frame.

They bought a house, with four bedrooms a mile from Oxford.

WARNING? No. Hikers are allowed in this restaurant.

I shall buy a car, in part-exchange for my wife.

Have your car serviced in one hour free. Oil included.

Now try this!

• **Write the meanings of each pair of sentences.**

Teachers' note These questions will help: Does the lady or the frame collapse? Were the bedrooms or the whole house a mile from Oxford? Are hikers allowed in the restaurant? Is the car for his wife? Is the oil or the service free?

**Developing Literacy
Sentence Level Year 5
© A & C Black 1999**

Punctuation changes 2

• **Punctuate these sentences to give two different meanings.**

Use full stops, commas, exclamation marks, question marks or speech marks.

Was Emma or the teacher speaking?

The teacher said Emma should be quiet

1._____

2._____

Was James going to eat or be eaten?

Come and eat James said Mum

1._____

2._____

Does Laura know Sunil?

I don't know Sunil said Laura

1._____

2._____

Who was asking the question?

Is this pen yours William asked Rosie

1._____

2._____

Is Kevin talking to Pilar?

Can you see Pilar called Kevin through the mist

1._____

2._____

Now try this!

• **Take turns with a partner to read the sentences aloud.**

Use the punctuation.

Teachers' note The children could copy sentences from books and then re-write them, punctuating them differently for a partner to read aloud and re-punctuate. To help their partners they could write hints like those in the speech bubbles.

**Developing Literacy
Sentence Level Year 5
© A & C Black 1999**

Using colons: sentence units

Each sentence on the printout is made up of
two units, but they have been mixed up.

Separate the units with a colon.

• Match the units and write the sentences.

I saw something strange in the sky / how to make bread. / a mobile phone. / I made a wish / She had an idea / a red light above the trees. / She had forgotten something / I learned something new today / for a pony. / He heard something buzzing in the cupboard / her glasses. / There was one important question / to have a new package designed for the biscuits. / who would be the new captain? /

I saw something strange in the sky: a red light above the trees.

_____

_____

_____

_____

_____

_____

_____

_____

_____

_____

Now try this!

• **Write another unit for each of these sentences:**

There was one thing he wanted to know.

She had a choice.

Teachers' note The children could also write their own sentences with two units. Useful openings include: 'He knew what to do', 'There was only one thing left in the bag', 'She had made up her mind', 'She made a guess'.

Developing Literacy
Sentence Level Year 5
© A & C Black 1999

Using colons: lists

• **Complete each sentence with a list.**

Remember the colon.

...and the commas.

...and the full stop.

Remember to buy these

_____

_____

4 vegetables

The following are forbidden _____

_____

_____

3 actions

MEMO
Sam, please fix these

_____

_____

4 parts of a car

These children play in the five-a-side football team

_____

_____

_____

5 first names

These are the cities I have visited _____

_____

_____

3 cities

These are the colours of the rainbow _____

_____

_____

_____

7 colours of the rainbow

I can see the following kinds of tree _____

_____

_____

_____

3 trees

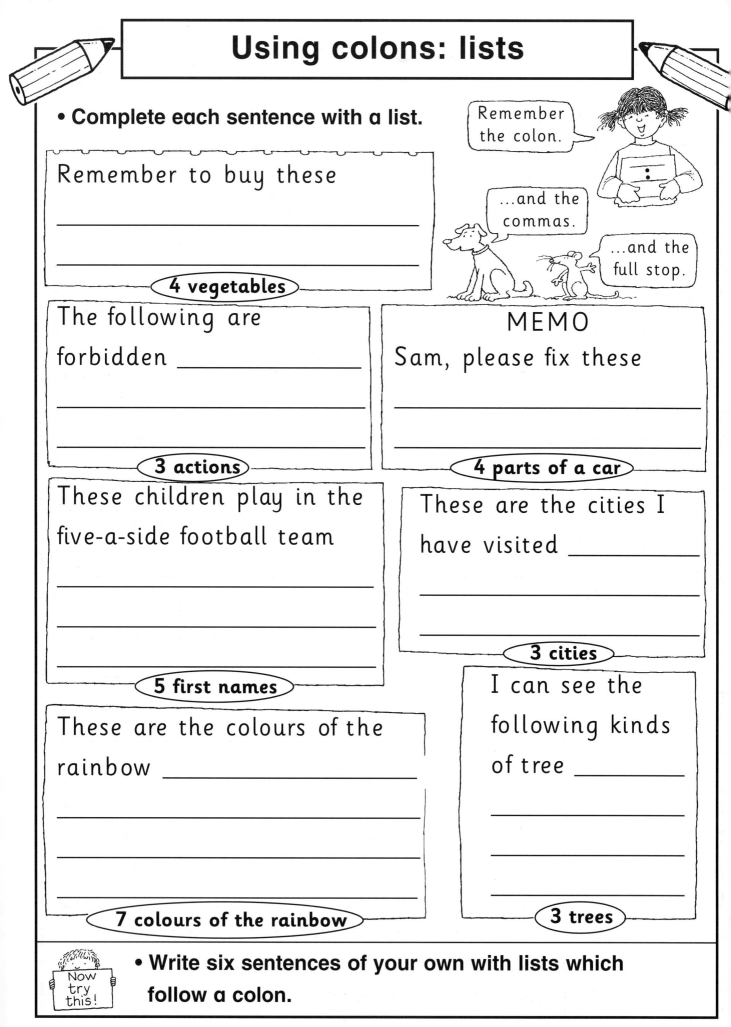

Now try this!

• **Write six sentences of your own with lists which follow a colon.**

Teachers' note The children could investigate the use of colons in non-fiction texts, deciding why each colon is used (for splitting a sentence into sections or to signal a list).

**Developing Literacy
Sentence Level Year 5
© A & C Black 1999**

Using semi-colons

- **Link the pairs of sentences which belong together.**
- **Re-write them as one sentence.**

Use a semi-colon in your sentence.

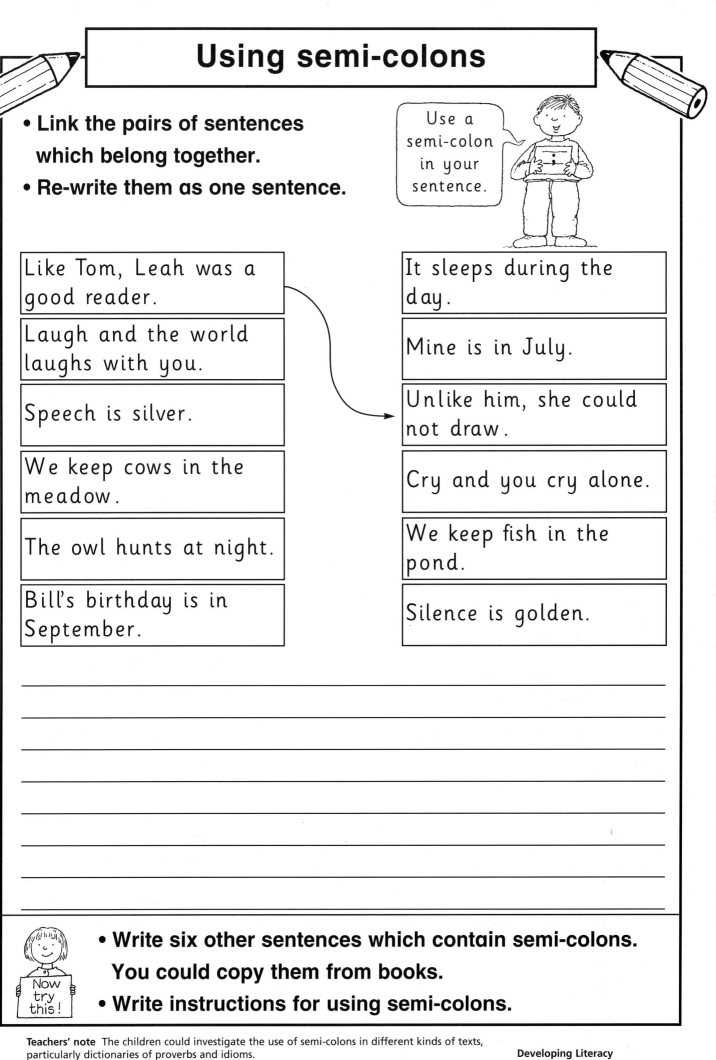

Like Tom, Leah was a good reader.	It sleeps during the day.
Laugh and the world laughs with you.	Mine is in July.
Speech is silver.	Unlike him, she could not draw.
We keep cows in the meadow.	Cry and you cry alone.
The owl hunts at night.	We keep fish in the pond.
Bill's birthday is in September.	Silence is golden.

Now try this!

- **Write six other sentences which contain semi-colons. You could copy them from books.**
- **Write instructions for using semi-colons.**

Teachers' note The children could investigate the use of semi-colons in different kinds of texts, particularly dictionaries of proverbs and idioms.

Developing Literacy
Sentence Level Year 5
© A & C Black 1999

Apostrophe idioms

• **Complete the chart with idioms which contain words with apostrophes.**

An idiom is a saying.

Use dictionaries of idioms and sayings.

Clue	Meaning	Idiom
fingers of the ladies	okra	ladies' fingers
Mother is the word.	Don't talk about it.	
the width of a hair	a very narrow gap	
At a distance which is the length of an arm	at a safe distance	
the choice of Hobson	No choice at all	
What is being cooked?	What is going on?	
The sky is the boundary.	infinity	
The joints of an insect which stings	the best	
Trouble is being brewed.	There will be trouble.	
tails belonging to rodents	straggly hair	
the eye belonging to Kelly	number one in a game of bingo	
a meal of a dog	an untidy mess	

Now try this!

• **On the chart, shade red the idioms in which the apostrophe shows possession, and shade blue those in which it shows missed out letters.**

Teachers' note Provide dictionaries of idioms and sayings. The children could continue the chart by writing the meanings of, and clues for, other idioms which they come across, for others to work out.

Developing Literacy
Sentence Level Year 5
© A & C Black 1999

42

Dialogue

- **Circle the incorrect punctuation in the passage.**
- **Re-write the passage, punctuating it correctly.**

What's that gasped "Raj What asked Sara following "his pointing finger I can't see anything Her "eyes were not yet used to the darkness. That! Look! There's something moving by the greenhouse hissed Raj". Something glided silently past the panes of glass which shone in the moonlight. Yes! I can see it now whispered Sara." Is it a fox Raj whispered no I don't think so It's too tall It's more like a small person, "perhaps a child". Raj looked towards the greenhouse. Oh he breathed There it is again Did you see it Sara? "Sara could not believe her eyes I saw it and I could see through it she said." Raj nodded his head A ghost they both whispered."

_____

_____

_____

_____

_____

_____

_____

_____

_____

_____

_____

Now try this!

- **With a partner, write some rules for punctuating dialogue.**

Teachers' note The children can describe the changes they made to the passage and why.

Developing Literacy
Sentence Level Year 5
© A & C Black 1999

Back to the future

• **Read about Shah Jahan's plan for the Taj Mahal.**

This temple shall be breathtakingly beautiful — built from white marble; it shall stand on the bank of the river and shall be set in lush green gardens with cool pools and fountains. It shall be perfectly symmetrical; a dome shall crown it and four minarets shall rise from its corners. The marble shall be inlaid with exquisite gems in floral patterns. The finest craftspeople shall carve inscriptions from the Holy Qur'an on the walls. A marble screen shall surround the tomb which shall stand in the centre of the chamber. Its lattice pattern shall filter and soften the sunlight so that a soft glow shall light the tomb.

• **Re-write the description in the present tense for a guidebook.**

_____

_____

_____

_____

_____

_____

_____

_____

_____

_____

_____

• **Re-write the description in the past tense, as a story.**

Teachers' note The children could also begin with a guide book (in the present tense) about another famous building and write their ideas (in the future tense) of the architect's dreams and plans.

Developing Literacy
Sentence Level Year 5
© A & C Black 1999

Using auxiliary verbs

● **Complete the verb chart.**

Have, has, am, are, is, was, were, shall and will are auxiliaries used with other verbs to form different tenses.

Person		Present	Future	Past		
I	skip	am skipping	shall skip	skipped	was skipping	have skipped
I	eat					
you	run	are running	will run	ran	were running	have run
you	drive					
he ✱	thinks	is thinking	will think			
he	rides					
she	writes					
it	rains					
we ✱	go	are going	shall go			
we	bring					
they	sing		will sing			
they	fly					

● **Write sentences which contain the verbs in the lines marked ✱.**

Example: He thinks he is the boss. He is thinking about the party.

Now try this!

Teachers' note On a copy of the chart (with the text in the tense columns deleted) the children could write the same tenses of other verbs: for example, to come, to drink, to seek, to hide and to sink.

Developing Literacy
Sentence Level Year 5
© A & C Black 1999

Active and passive verbs

Both these sentences have the same meaning:

a) The girl ate the fish.

b) The fish was eaten by the girl.

In a) the verb is active ; in b) it is passive .

• **For each picture, write a sentence with an active verb.**

• **Re-write the sentence, making the verb passive.**

_____

_____

_____

_____

_____

_____

_____

_____

_____

_____

_____

_____

Now try this!

• **Write four sentences with the following active verbs:**

broke, caught, is singing, will make.

• **Re-write the sentences, making the verbs passive.**

Teachers' note During the plenary session the children could describe how to make an active verb passive, noting changes such as ate/eaten, the addition of 'by', the exchanged positions of the subject and object of the verb and what is done to whom or what by whom or what.

**Developing Literacy
Sentence Level Year 5
© A & C Black 1999**

Interrogative forms of verbs

The <u>interrogative</u> form of a verb is used in questions.

Examples: | Shall I wash | the car?

| Did you post | the letter?

- **Change the verbs into their interrogative forms.**
- **Write the questions in the speech bubbles.**

1. Your name is Robin Banks.

2. You were driving a Ford Sierra on Monday 2nd of May.

3. It was a pale blue car.

4. You parked it in the High Street.

5. Three men got into the car at 9pm.

6. You drove North towards the motorway.

7. You stopped in West Woods.

8. One of the men handed you a case.

- **Write about how you changed the verb in each sentence.**

Now try this!

Think about word order, changed words and additional words.

Teachers' note The children could also change statements in the present and future tenses into questions. They could explore and compare the ways in which verbs change; for example, 'you did'/'did you?' but not 'you ran'/'ran you?'.

Developing Literacy
Sentence Level Year 5
© A & C Black 1999

Imperative forms of verbs

The <u>imperative</u> form of a verb is used in a command, an order or an instruction.

Sit!

Please queue here

DANGER KEEP OUT

Walk on, through the wind. Walk on, through the rain...

• **Re-write the statements using the imperative form of the verb.**

You must stop, thief.

You may cross.

You should buy now.

You must not fish.

You should take a basket.

You should make your way to the checkouts.

You should leave your message after the tone.

• **Write a set of instructions for visitors to a zoo.**

Now try this!

Tell people what they must and must <u>not</u> do.

• **Re-write them as statements.**

Teachers' note Encourage the children to notice that imperatives are always in the second person (because instructions, orders or commands are always addressed to someone or something).

Developing Literacy Sentence Level Year 5 © A & C Black 1999

Instructions

- **Read the account about setting a video recorder.**
- **Re-write it as a set of instructions.**

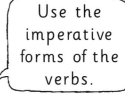

Use the imperative forms of the verbs.

First I inserted the video cassette. Then I chose the television channel of the programme to be recorded, using the arrow keys. Then the channel number was displayed. After that I set the recording speed by pressing the button marked SP/LP (standard play or long play). I pressed the REC (record) button and held it down for two seconds to start recording. I then pressed REC several times until the correct recording time was shown. I chose 1 hour, because that was the length of the programme.

Insert the video cassette.

_____

_____

_____

_____

_____

_____

_____

_____

_____

_____

_____

_____

Now try this!

- **Write six rules for good behaviour, using the imperative forms of the verbs.**
- **Re-write the rules as an account about good behaviour.**

Teachers' note The children should first complete page 48. In the extension activity they could convert school or classroom rules into statements: for example, 'Be kind to others'/ 'We are kind to others'.

**Developing Literacy
Sentence Level Year 5
© A & C Black 1999**

Person to person

• **Re-write 'The Cuckoo' in the** third person singular.

Cuckoo, cuckoo,   _____

What do you do?   _____

In April   _____

I open my bill.   _____

In May   _____

I sing night and day.   _____

In June   _____

I change my tune.   _____

In July   _____

Away I fly.   _____

In August   _____

Go I must.   _____

(ANONYMOUS)

• **Re-write this verse in the** second person plural.

By the rivers of Babylon, there we sat down,
Yea, we wept, when we remembered Zion.
We hung our harps upon the willows
In the midst thereof.

(PSALM 137, FROM THE AUTHORISED VERSION OF THE BIBLE)

_____

_____

_____

_____

Now try this!

• **Make charts on which to record the classes of words you changed in each verse.**

Pronouns	Verbs

Teachers' note For the extension activity it might help to have a separate chart for each text. The children should notice that the pronouns for the object as well as the subject change, and so do any possessive pronouns; the verbs also change.

Developing Literacy
Sentence Level Year 5
© A & C Black 1999

From voice to paper 1

- **Write the dialogue for a reader who can not see the pictures.**

Think about punctuation, and underlining or capital letters for emphasis.

Think about adverbs, and different words for 'said'.

Goodbye. We're off to the disco.

I wish I could go to the disco.

You can! Switch off that iron or there will be a big insurance claim, and listen to me.

Who are you?

I'm your fairy godmother. Now here's my plan of action.

<u>"Goodbye. We're off to the disco," announced...</u>

_____

_____

_____

_____

_____

_____

_____

_____

Now try this!

- **With a partner, enact another scene from the story.**
- **Write the dialogue.**

Teachers' note After watching one another enacting the picture story the children can discuss the best words to use for 'said' and (if necessary) adverbs which best describe how the words are said.

**Developing Literacy
Sentence Level Year 5
© A & C Black 1999**

From voice to paper 2

• **Write the dialogue for a reader who can not see the pictures.**

Teachers' note The children could make up, enact and write other dialogues from historical events in a way which conveys the speakers' feelings to the reader.

Developing Literacy
Sentence Level Year 5
© A & C Black 1999

Advertisement sentences

- **Read the advertisements.**
- **Re-write them in complete sentences.**

A sentence must contain a verb.

① SPECIAL OFFER
FREE
250 g strawberries with every 500 ml carton of cream

1._____
_____
_____

② SALE
Last day
Everything ½ price

2._____
_____
_____

③ FAMILY PACK
Seven bags for the price of six
CRISPS

3._____
_____
_____

④ FOR SALE
1994 SAAB 900
70,000 miles
One owner £12,000

4._____
_____
_____

⑤ Best quality beds
Lowest prices in town
Unbeatable service
Free delivery

5._____
_____
_____
_____

Now try this!

- **Highlight the words which you added.**
- **Make a chart to record what classes of words they are.**

Verbs	Pronouns	Other kinds of words
is	you	this
can	we	the

Teachers' note Encourage the children to notice the words which are omitted from the advertisement sentences; for example, 'Special offer'/'This is a special offer'. They could try writing their own 'advertising copy'.

Developing Literacy
Sentence Level Year 5
© A & C Black 1999

Summarising

A **summary** contains the main points of a text.

It leaves out the details.

- **Link the summaries to the texts.**

> The airport was closed because members of the cabin crews were on strike. This made people who were going on holiday angry.

> Police have caught the wild dog which has been terrorising Toptown people.

> The road was blocked by farm animals.

> Holidaymakers were angered by the cabin crew strike which closed the airport.

> A wild dog has been causing terror among the people of Toptown. They have been afraid to go outside in case they were attacked. Now the police have caught the dog and everyone feels safe.

> Drivers could not use the road because cows, pigs and sheep were wandering across it.

- **Write a one-sentence summary of each paragraph.**

Do not stand while the aircraft is landing. Remain in your seats until it is on the ground.

_____
_____
_____

These animals may be fed only by the keepers. Do not feed them or you will have to pay a fine.

_____
_____
_____

Our store detectives are watching for thieves. If they catch anyone stealing our goods they will arrest him or her.

_____
_____
_____

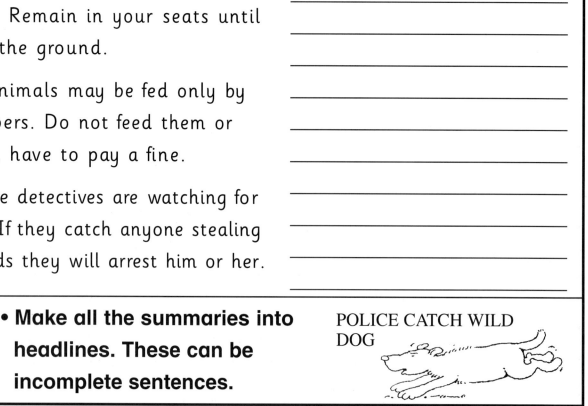

- **Make all the summaries into headlines. These can be incomplete sentences.**

POLICE CATCH WILD DOG

Teachers' note The children could write summaries of their accounts of investigations in other subjects, such as science, geography and history, to fit into a given space: for instance, a column of a class newspaper.

Developing Literacy
Sentence Level Year 5
© A & C Black 1999

At a glance

- **Highlight the essential information in the science notebook.**
- **Write this information on the chart.**

We looked at the colours of the metals. Brass and copper are yellow, lead is dark grey; steel, aluminium, iron and zinc are whitish-grey. We tried to bend the metals. Only lead could be bent with bare hands. Steel and iron are magnetic, but the other metals are not. They all conduct electricity. We put the metal discs in water. They all sank. We left them in a damp place. Iron and steel went rusty, aluminium went white and lead went green; the others did not change.

Metal	Colour	Bends with bare hands	Magnetic	Conducts electricity	Floats	Effects of damp
brass	yellow	no	no	yes	no	no change

Now try this!

- **Make a chart on which to record this information:**

We compared floor surfaces. Crockery broke when dropped on vinyl, wood and quarry tiles. It did not break when dropped on carpet, carpet tiles or cushioned vinyl. Carpet, carpet tiles and cushioned vinyl felt warm under bare feet; the others felt cold. Only carpet was comfortable to sit on. We could easily brush crumbs from vinyl, wood, quarry tiles and cushioned vinyl, but not from the others.

Teachers' note The children could compare the two methods of communicating information and decide which is the better for this type of information and why.

Developing Literacy
Sentence Level Year 5
© A & C Black 1999

55

Sleeker sentences

Sometimes a text can be improved by combining two or more sentences.

Example:

She had stripped the walls and mixed the paste. She could begin wallpapering.	→	Having stripped the walls and mixed the paste, she could begin wallpapering.

• **Find ways in which to combine these sentences:**

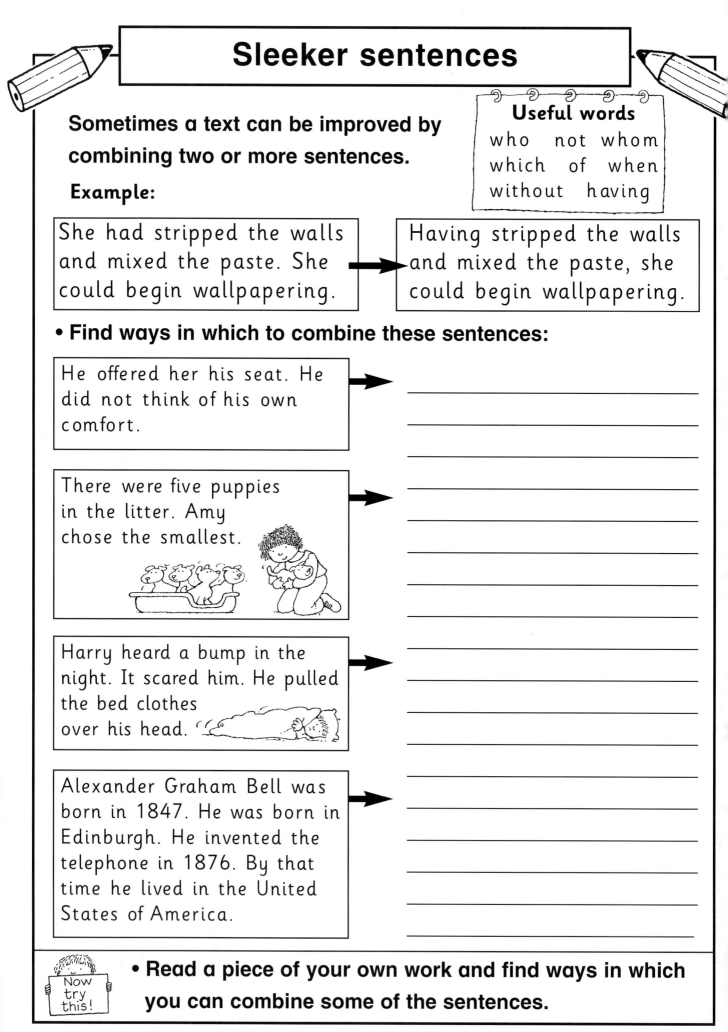

He offered her his seat. He did not think of his own comfort.   →   _____

There were five puppies in the litter. Amy chose the smallest.   →   _____

Harry heard a bump in the night. It scared him. He pulled the bed clothes over his head.   →   _____

Alexander Graham Bell was born in 1847. He was born in Edinburgh. He invented the telephone in 1876. By that time he lived in the United States of America.   →   _____

Now try this!

• **Read a piece of your own work and find ways in which you can combine some of the sentences.**

Teachers' note The children could write simple sentences which answer questions about a person or thing and then combine them to make 'sleeker' sentences.

Developing Literacy
Sentence Level Year 5
© A & C Black 1999

Sentence-building game

- Cut out the sentence-strips along the dotted lines.
- The first player writes an adjective in the first box, folds it over and passes the strip to the second player.
- The second player writes a noun in the second box, folds it over and passes the strip to the third player, and so on.
- Open out the sentence-strip and read the sentence. (You might need to add 'a', 'an' or 'the'.)
- Write the complete sentences.

Don't let anyone see what you have written!

Adjective	Noun	Adverb	Verb	Adjective	Noun
Adjective	Noun	Adverb	Verb	Adjective	Noun
Adjective	Noun	Adverb	Verb	Adjective	Noun
Adjective	Noun	Adverb	Verb	Adjective	Noun

Teachers' note During the plenary session the children could read out their sentences. Discuss word-order – what happens if they use sentence-strips with the word classes in a different order?

Developing Literacy
Sentence Level Year 5
© A & C Black 1999

Re-ordering sentences

- **Sometimes you can improve your writing by changing the order of the words in a sentence.**

> You might have to change some of the words when you re-order a sentence.

Example:

| I missed the bus so I was late and I could not go to the football match. | → | Because I missed the bus, I was too late to go to the football match. |

- **Re-order the sentences so that they read better.**

| We walked a long way in the hot sunshine and got thirsty and wished we had taken some water with us. | → | _____ |

| We went shopping and then we went swimming and then we had lunch. | → | _____ |

| Bip arrived first and Jack came just a few minutes later and Hannah came after an hour. | → | _____ |

| I like apples and William likes apples too, but Joe does not like them. | → | _____ |

Now try this!

- **Re-order each of the sentences in a different way.**

Teachers' note The children could look for sentences in their own writing to edit in this way.

**Developing Literacy
Sentence Level Year 5**
© A & C Black 1999

Types of phrases

Developing Literacy
Sentence Level Year 5
© A & C Black 1999

- Link each <u>noun phrase</u> with an <u>adjective phrase</u>.
- Add an interesting verb and make a sentence.

A phrase can not make sense on its own as a sentence.

Noun phrases	Adjective phrases
Jodie's cousin	much louder
the sound of the drill	very clever
her engagement ring	quite exciting
the football match	bright with stars
Jack's beanstalk	completely ruined
the silver tray	sparkling with jewels
the night sky	numb with cold
explorers of the Arctic	extremely shiny
part of the old temple	taller and taller

Jodie's cousin seems to be very clever. _____

_____

_____

_____

_____

_____

_____

_____

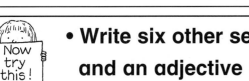
Now try this!

- **Write six other sentences which contain a noun phrase and an adjective phrase.**

Teachers' note The children could make up adjective phrases to describe things in the classroom.

Clause links

- **Make sentences using a clause from each list and a connective.**

A clause contains a verb. It can make sense as a sentence.

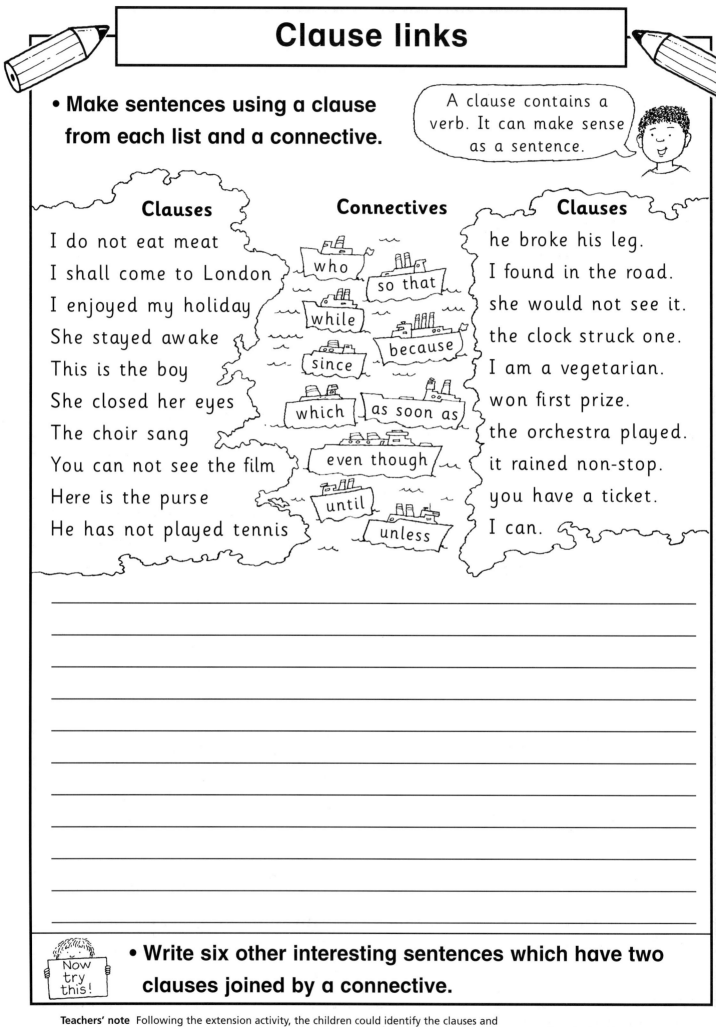

Clauses

I do not eat meat
I shall come to London
I enjoyed my holiday
She stayed awake
This is the boy
She closed her eyes
The choir sang
You can not see the film
Here is the purse
He has not played tennis

Connectives

who
so that
while
because
since
which
as soon as
even though
until
unless

Clauses

he broke his leg.
I found in the road.
she would not see it.
the clock struck one.
I am a vegetarian.
won first prize.
the orchestra played.
it rained non-stop.
you have a ticket.
I can.

- **Write six other interesting sentences which have two clauses joined by a connective.**

Now try this!

Teachers' note Following the extension activity, the children could identify the clauses and connectives in one another's sentences.

Developing Literacy
Sentence Level Year 5
© A & C Black 1999

Main clause

The <u>main clause</u> is the main part of a sentence.
It makes sense on its own.

Example: | The cat purred | whenever it was happy.

• **Draw a box round the main clause in each sentence.**

1. I shall come and see you as soon as I can.

2. The girls were good friends who lived near to one another.

3. She stared at the blank page as if a picture might appear on it.

4. They went to the museum, where they saw a dinosaur's skeleton.

The following sentences have more than one main clause.

• **Draw boxes round the main clauses.**

5. We went to the park and we met our friends.

6. The sun shone and the wind blew.

7. I caught the train, I went to London and I did some shopping.

8. Dad bought a coat, Mum bought some shoes, Zul bought a book and I bought nothing.

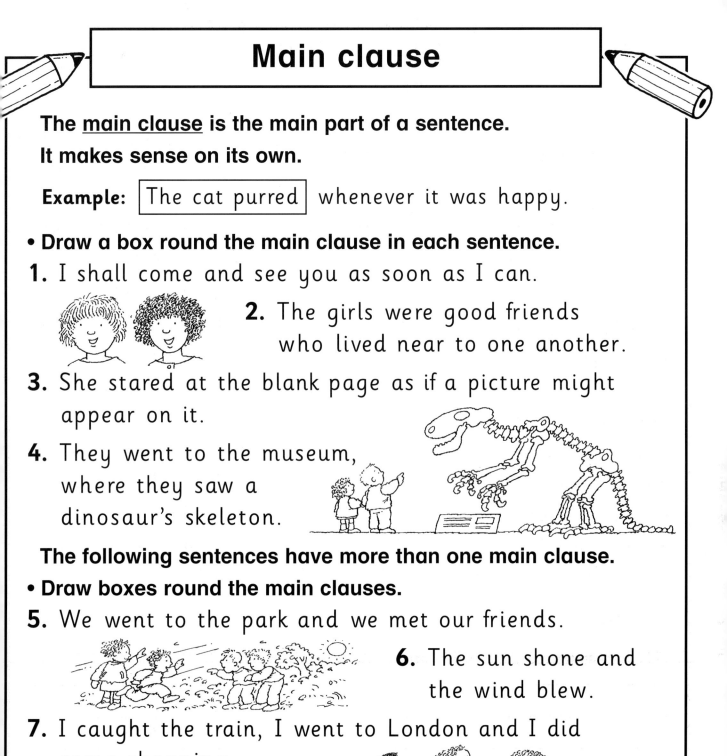

• **Write three sentences which have two main clauses.**
• **Write three sentences which have a main clause and another clause.**

Now try this!

Teachers' note The children might first need to practise identifying the main and subordinate clauses of sentences in a shared text.

Developing Literacy
Sentence Level Year 5
© A & C Black 1999

Clause sandwiches

The main clause can make a sandwich around another clause in a sentence.

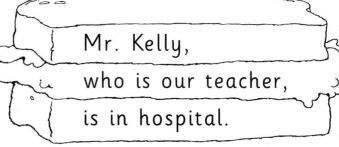

Mr. Kelly,
who is our teacher,
is in hospital.

The clause in the middle is called an 'embedded clause'.
It is surrounded by commas:

Mr. Kelly, who is our teacher, is in hospital.

- **Write the sentences on the sandwiches.**

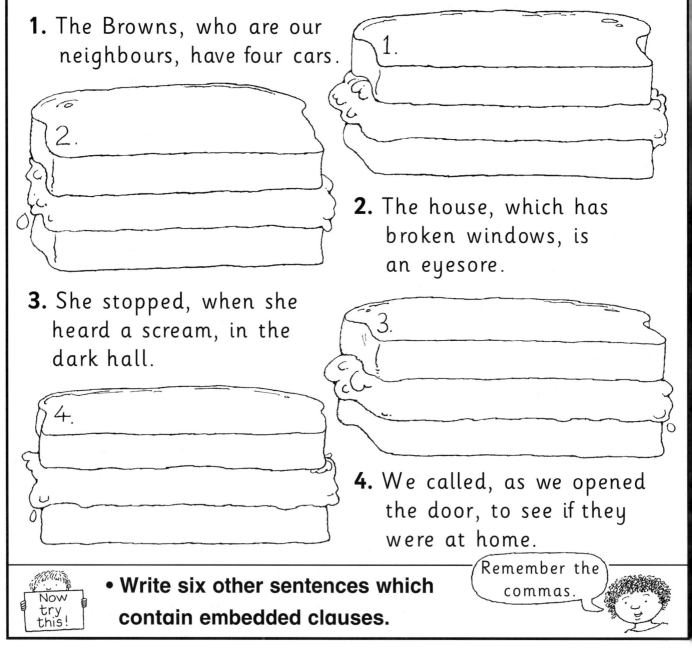

1. The Browns, who are our neighbours, have four cars.

2. The house, which has broken windows, is an eyesore.

3. She stopped, when she heard a scream, in the dark hall.

4. We called, as we opened the door, to see if they were at home.

Now try this!

- **Write six other sentences which contain embedded clauses.**

Remember the commas.

Teachers' note To help the children to identify the main clause in each sentence, encourage them to read it omitting the clause between the commas.

**Developing Literacy
Sentence Level Year 5
© A & C Black 1999**

Ambiguity

Ambiguity means 'double meaning'.

Example: The shop was empty except for a woman carrying a baby and a security guard.

or

• **Re-write the above sentence twice, to make its two possible meanings clear.**

_____

_____

_____

_____

• **Re-write the headlines and signs twice, to make their two possible meanings clear.**

POLICE CATCH THIEF IN ROLLS ROYCE

_____

BABY CHANGING ROOM

_____

BUS ON FIRE PASSENGERS ALIGHT

_____

WOMAN ESCAPES WITH MONET

The RSPB Farmland Birds Draw

_____

Now try this!

• **Look for other examples of ambiguity.**
• **Re-write them to make their two possible meanings clear.**

Teachers' note The children could look for ambiguity in everyday texts such as newspaper headlines, signs, labels and notices. Some newspapers publish collections of ambiguous texts.

**Developing Literacy
Sentence Level Year 5
© A & C Black 1999**

Ambiguous pronouns

- **Re-write these texts so that they are not ambiguous.**
- **Underline the problem pronouns.**

You could change the order of parts of the text, add words and even change the number of sentences.

"We saw the deer during our walk," said Ann, adding that they were wearing stout walking boots.

Today's tip tells you how to have lovely skin. Cut it out, glue it on to card and keep it on your dressing table.

The woman brought her dog; she was small, with big feet and long ears.

The explosives were discovered by sniffer dogs. They were hidden in ice cream cartons.

Children are damaging the flower beds. I blame parents and teachers. They play chasing games there.

If the baby does not like raw apple, stew it gently for five minutes.

Now try this!

- **Write the two possible meanings for each of the texts (even though one meaning might be silly!)**

Teachers' note Encourage the children to make a habit of editing their own writing with a view to removing ambiguity.

Developing Literacy
Sentence Level Year 5
© A & C Black 1999